HAMMERED METALWORK

An Introduction to
DECORATIVE WOODWORK

By

HERBERT H. GRIMWOOD
Principal of the School of Wood
Carving, South Kensington,

and

FREDERICK GOODYEAR
Craft Master, Chatham House
(County) School, Ramsgate;
Fellow of the College of
Handicraft.

A BOOK for all who are
interested in the Craft of Woodwork, and especially for those
who teach it in Schools.

Fully Illustrated   20/- net

Metalwork by Goldsmiths' College Students during a One-year Course.

HAMMERED METALWORK

By

T. FRANKLIN EVANS

Lecturer in Hand Craft and Art, Goldsmiths' College,
University of London. Lecturer and Tutor
in Metalwork for the Board of Education.

With a Foreword by

H. G. MURPHY

Principal, Central School of Arts and Crafts, London
County Council, Southampton Row,
London, W.C.

With Frontispiece and 76 plates
in Line and Half-tone

UNIVERSITY OF LONDON PRESS, LTD.
10 & 11 WARWICK LANE, LONDON, E.C.4

FIRST PRINTED . . *July* 1936

Printed in Great Britain for the UNIVERSITY OF LONDON PRESS, LTD.,
by HAZELL, WATSON AND VINEY, LTD., London and Aylesbury.

FOREWORD

A GOOD book needs no foreword, and this book is a good one. It differs materially from so many books on craft which are written for amateurs by amateurs. Mr. Evans has devoted his life to his subject and he has brought to bear on his work a logical and precise mind. He has set out in order a practical and efficient method of instruction for the use of teachers of metalwork.

Such a book comes at an opportune time, when the importance of Hand Craft as a means of teaching appreciation of design is becoming more widely recognized. "Training in metalwork can and should at the same time constitute a lesson in design, that is to say, in a sense of good proportion, of logical construction and of the right use of materials," states the Council of Art and Industry in *Education for the Consumer*.

Lack of method has perhaps been the deficiency in most attempts at teaching metalwork to the young, and good method is necessary if the subject is not to become tedious. It is well, therefore, that there should be available to those engaged in teaching or about to teach metalwork a standard of instruction. This, I consider, Mr. Evans has produced.

As a text-book it will be invaluable, not only to the teacher but also to the student. Unlike most text-books it does not repeat the errors of its predecessors, but is full of direct information that can only be imparted after years of devotion and careful thought. It should find a place in Art and Craft schools, Training Colleges, Technical, Secondary and Elementary schools and will be a source of inspiration wherever hand craft is taught.

H. G. MURPHY.
Principal, Central School of Arts and Crafts,
London County Council,
Southampton Row, London, W.C.

June 1936.

ACKNOWLEDGMENTS

A SELECTION from the Board of Education Courses in Hand Craft, 1930–1936, is contained in Chapter XXIX. It consists of examples of metalwork designed and used by the author to form the practical work of the Hammered Metalwork Courses and is included by permission of A. S. Bright, Esq., H.M.I., Staff Inspector of Hand Craft, Board of Education.

I am grateful to Dr. A. Platts, M.A., H.M.I., for valuable suggestions, and to H. Moorhouse, Esq., also of His Majesty's Inspectorate, for helpful criticism.

To the Warden of Goldsmiths' College, A. E. Dean, Esq., M.A., M.Litt., to G. J. Cons, Esq., M.A., Dr. W. Rees, M.A., and to many other of my colleagues, I am indebted for much assistance willingly given.

T. FRANKLIN EVANS.

Goldsmiths' College,
University of London,
1936.

CONTENTS

CHAPTER   PAGE

FOREWORD v

ACKNOWLEDGMENTS vii

INTRODUCTION xiii

I. THE PROCESSES OF HAMMERED METALWORK . . . I

II. THE WORKSHOP AND ITS EQUIPMENT . . . 6

III. MATERIALS. 14

IV. DRAWING 19

V. ESTIMATING INITIAL DIMENSIONS AND ALLOWANCES. 23

VI. PREPARATION AND CARE OF METAL SURFACES . 27

VII. SETTING-OUT 35

VIII. CUTTING PROCESSES 39

IX. HEATING METHODS 44

X. BENDING 50

XI. FOLDING 52

XII. HOLLOWING 55

XIII. SINKING 58

XIV. STRETCHING 61

XV. CONTRACTING 65

XVI. PRODUCTION OF SEAMED FORMS . . . 67

XVII. RAISING 69

XVIII. PLANISHING 76

XIX. TESTING METHODS 82

XX. METHODS OF TRUING AND ADJUSTING . . 85

XXI. FILING AND FITTING 89

XXII. SOFT-SOLDERING 94

XXIII. SILVER-SOLDERING 103

XXIV. HINGING 119

XXV. TREATMENT OF EDGES 123

XXVI. POLISHING AND COLOURING PROCESSES . . 132

XXVII. DECORATION 137

XXVIII. CONSTRUCTED AND IMPROVISED EQUIPMENT . 142

XXIX. EXAMPLES OF PRACTICAL WORK . . . 156

XXX. THE TEACHING OF HAMMERED METALWORK . 183

LIST OF PLATES

METALWORK BY GOLDSMITHS' COLLEGE STUDENTS . *Frontispiece*

I. PROCESSES

PLATE   PAGE

1. POINTS OF CONTACT AND IMPACT 197
2. HAMMERS 198
3. LARGE STAKES 199
4. PATTERN DRAWING 200
5. PATTERN DRAWING (*continued*) 201
6. ESTIMATING INITIAL DIMENSIONS . . . 202
7. PREPARATION OF METAL SURFACES . . . 203
8. SETTING-OUT ON METAL 204
9. CUTTING METHODS 205
10. CUTTING METHODS (*continued*) 206
11. CUTTING METHODS (*continued*) 207
12. BLOWPIPE CONTROL 208
13. BENDING 209
14. BENT WIRE HANDLE 210
15. FOLDING 211
16. HOLLOWING 212
17. HOLLOWED FORMS 213
18. SINKING 214
19. STRETCHING 215
20. CONTRACTING 216
21. SEAMED FORMS 217
22. RAISING WITH MALLET 218
23. RAISING WITH HAMMER 219
24. RAISING 220

PLATE   PAGE

25. PANELLING AND CAULKING 221
26. RAISED FORMS 222
27. ACTION OF RAISING PROCESS 223
28. PLANISHING 224
29. PLANISHING (continued) 225
30. TESTING METHODS 226
31. TRUING AND ADJUSTING 227
32. TRUING AND ADJUSTING (continued) 228
33. FILING AND FITTING 229
34. HANDLE FITTING 230
35. SOFT-SOLDERING 231
36. SOFT-SOLDERING (continued) 232
37. SILVER-SOLDERING 233
38. SILVER-SOLDERING (continued) 234
39. SILVER-SOLDERING (continued) 235
40. HINGING 236
41. HINGING (continued) 237
42. EDGE-FOLDING 238
43. EDGE-WIRING 239
44. WIRE TWISTING AND PLAITING 240
45. SURFACE DECORATION 241

2. CONSTRUCTED EQUIPMENT

46. HARDWOOD EQUIPMENT 242
47. IMPROVISED SURFACE-PLATE 243
48. SOLDERING HEARTH 244
49. PETROL VAPORIZER 245
50. SMALL STEEL TOOLS 246
51. HAMMERS 247
52. STAKES 248

3. WORKING DRAWINGS AND PHOTOGRAPHS

PLATE

53 and 65. SMALL TRAY, PIN BOWL, NAPKIN RING, PAGE
    TUMBLER STAND . . . . 249 and 261

54 and 66. PIERCED RING, HEPTAGONAL TRAY, SMALL
    VASE, HOLLOWED TRAY . . . 250 and 262

55 and 67. HEXAGONAL PLATE, RAISED TRAY, CADDY
    SPOON, HOLLOWED BOWL . . . 251 and 263

56 and 68. TANKARD, SEAMED VASE, CIRCULAR DISH . 252 and 264

57 and 69. TEAPOT STAND, ASH BOWL, CANISTER,
    HOLLOWED DISH . . . . 253 and 265

58 and 70. SMALL TANKARD, BEAKER, WIRED PLATE,
    COVERED PLATE . . . . 254 and 266

59 and 71. INKSTAND, RAISED BOWL, CIGARETTE BOX 255 and 267

60 and 72. SWEETS DISH, TEA CADDY, TRINKET BOX. 256 and 268

61 and 73. CANDLESTICK, OCTAGONAL BOX, POWDER
    BOWL, RAISED VASE . . . 257 and 269

62 and 74. TEAPOT AND STAND, SUGAR BOWL . . 258 and 270

63 and 74. HOT-WATER JUG, CREAM JUG . . . 259 and 270

64 and 75. FRUIT STAND. . . . . . 260 and 271

76. RAISED SILVER VASE 272

INTRODUCTION

HAMMERED metalwork is the term herein used to denote constructive silversmithing and the extension of its hand processes to suitable non-ferrous base metals. It embraces the hand-tool operations involved in the construction of domestic ware in Silver, Gilding-metal, Copper and Brass.

To write of hand methods might appear in this mechanized civilization to be a retrograde step, especially as the working of metal is concerned, the processes of which have been transformed by the merciless ingenuity of the machine.

In bygone days a craftsman prospered by the skill of his hand, but now the current flows so swiftly that those who rely solely upon hand methods soon become engulfed in its vortex.

Work in a hand craft to-day is but the retracing of the stream of development. To linger awhile in its backwaters is to find a stimulus which should inspire and influence design in the modern rapids of mass-production.

To design and make by hand something of simple beauty and usefulness, to make it well, sparing nothing in the making, is to recapture the spirit which animated those to whom we owe our heritage of fine craft-work.

Creative work in the hand crafts is still desirable and the acquiring of skill in a constructive craft is a wise employment of leisure. It encourages a balanced conception of design and its value in setting standards of taste is considerable.

It is insufficient to assess modern production with a revolution-counter and a stop-watch, or yet to assume that what is modern must of necessity be good. An urgent present-day requirement is that design for the machine shall be such that will make mass-production as inspired and genuine as hand work in the days of the craftsman of old. Experience in the hand crafts and a realization of the requirements of simplicity in modern design is a useful equipment for this task.

In hammered metalwork the hand processes are still available, and for those who find pleasure in working with their hands it is confidently stated that no more fascinating craft exists. The joy of shaping and seeing a disc of metal ' grow ' under the hammer, surprise at the unexpected beauty of an intermediate stage and the expression of the maker's personality in the finished work, may be the rewards of the modern hand-worker in metal as much to-day as they were to medieval workers.

A brief presentation of a hand craft imposes many perplexities. The first essential in any craft is that its main processes and tool-operations are thoroughly understood. This is the disciplinary side and it involves much setting down of method and rules before expressional and creative work can be considered. This latter aspect is the more interesting and the temptation is to go for this ultimate goal at the earliest moment. To fix a balance and finally to decide what shall be included and omitted is a matter requiring much consideration.

Hammered metalwork is often thought of as a craft which requires years of determined effort before the subtleties of its technique can be acquired. It would be untrue to state that little skill is required in the more advanced processes, nevertheless it is suggested that difficulties arise because the processes and tool-operations are not separated and their effects studied and understood in the early stages of the work.

It is realized that in the apparent similarity of the method of executing some of its main processes, hammered metalwork has a difficulty which is not shared by many other crafts. Several of its processes consist in the striking of the metal, supported on a steel stake or anvil, with a hammer. The appearance of each process is very similar and to an onlooker the same operation can produce a variety of widely differing results, suggesting that a subtle knack in the use of the hammer must be acquired before the desired result can be obtained.

Actually, these processes are quite separate and distinct, their results being governed by differences in the shape of hammer and stake faces or by the way in which the metal is held on the stake or is struck with the hammer.

The term ' beaten ' metalwork is frequently used. This is unfortunate, as sheet metal is not beaten into shape in the way the term sometimes suggests. It is shaped by definite processes, in a definite way, using definite tools.

The craft is also handicapped by a vagueness of terms applied generally to its processes and tools, many of which are known by a variety of names in text-books and toolmakers' catalogues.   There is little wonder that the shaping processes are sometimes confused as a result.

Unless the tool operations and processes are thoroughly understood, no rapid progress can be made, and in view of the foregoing considerations this volume gives the constructional side of the work the most attention. An attempt has been made to deal with each operation and process separately in as direct a way as possible.

It is not suggested that the methods indicated are the only ones available.   Very frequently no ' best ' method exists.   Two or more craftsmen may execute a job by different methods, yet they will all achieve the same standard of excellence in their finished work.

In the case of beginners, however, there is frequently a definite choice.   Of two or three possible methods, one may be the easiest or safest, or its action and effect may be more readily understood.   Where a choice has existed, these are the considerations which have decided the method to be described.

The educational handwork aspect of hammered metalwork has also influenced the choice of particular methods and materials.   If the traditional processes are always rigidly insisted upon, then much of the work is at once placed beyond the reach of the young pupil for reasons of cost and difficulty in execution.   It is claimed, however, that concessions in this direction—for example, the use of soft-solder and the production of tall forms by seaming instead of by raising from the flat, in early work in the base metals—do not materially lower the standard of the work. Rather do they widen its scope and give opportunity for experience in more advanced work in school and college workshops than would otherwise be possible.   In addition, they permit of comparison being made with the traditional methods which are used in the later work.

An extensive range of examples of hammered metalwork is included with brief working notes.   Nothing is claimed for this course of work, except that it provides experience in the processes described.

This presentation of the elements of hammered metalwork is commended to teachers of hand craft as a book of reference and to student-craftsmen as a classification and description of the fundamental processes and basic tool-operations of the craft, followed by suggestions for practice in acquiring the skill which alone can serve as a foundation for creative work.

elaborate is necessary, the chief requirements being the accurate indication of the finished shape and size of each part of the work and that the arrangement of all the joints is clearly shown. The estimation of the initial dimensions of the material is also a part of the preliminary drawing and consists of plotting therefrom the patterns which will represent the commencing shape and size of each part of the work. This may be simply a direct estimation or calculation from the dimensions of the drawing, though sometimes a second surface-development drawing is necessary.

2. PREPARATION AND CARE OF SURFACES

Under this heading are the processes which prepare the metal for working and also which maintain the surfaces in good condition during working. These include Annealing, or the softening of metal by heating; Pickling with dilute acid for the purpose of cleaning and removing impurities from the surface; Scouring with a fine abrasive and finally Flatting and the removal of small blemishes.

3. SETTING-OUT

Lines are applied to the material which act as guides in the subsequent cutting and shaping operations.

4. CUTTING

The metal is cut by definite methods applicable to sheet, strip and wire. Non-metallic material is also cut by particular methods.

5. SHAPING PROCESSES AND PLANISHING

Depending upon the required form of the work, the metal is shaped by one of the following processes, using a hammer or mallet, the work being supported on a steel anvil of a suitable shape called a stake, or on a shaped wood block or a leather bag filled with sand, known as a sand-pad.

Three methods are principally used for the production of shaped forms:—

(*a*) Low, shallow forms are obtained by either Hollowing or Sinking.

(*b*) Tall or deep forms are produced by Raising from the flat sheet of metal.

(*c*) An alternative method of producing tall forms is by Folding or Bending sheet metal and then jointing the edges in a seam. The shaping of this three-dimensional form is executed by processes of Stretching or Contracting.

In order to avoid confusion of these processes it is necessary to understand correctly the action of the tools involved and what is of equal importance, the correct methods of using them. These are considered in detail in the succeeding chapters on the shaping processes and only brief definitions are included at this stage.

Bending and Folding

When metal is shaped in one dimension only, it is either bent or folded. Bending produces curves and Folding gives corners. (A napkin-ring is usually made from a strip of metal, the ends of which are jointed. A circular ring would be bent and a hexagonal one folded.)

Hollowing

A shallow form, curved in two dimensions (e.g. a low circular bowl), is produced from a flat disc of sheet metal by being hollowed or depressed on its upper and inner surface.

Sinking

Sinking is a process of hollowing applied to a disc of flat metal in which the depression is in the centre of a flat margin or rim (as in a tray or plate).

Raising

Forms of any shape may be produced by the process of Raising from a flat disc of sheet metal, the operation being executed on the lower and outer surface of the disc.

Stretching

When the original diameter of a previously shaped form is increased, it is executed by a process of stretching, worked either externally or internally.

Contracting

A decrease in the diameter of a previously shaped form is obtained by an application of a contraction process and is executed externally.

Planishing

The process of truing-up by hammering which follows a shaping operation is termed planishing.

6. FITTING, ASSEMBLING AND JOINTING

This group of processes is concerned with the testing, truing and adjusting, filing, fitting and assembling of work consisting of two or more parts. Fixed joints are made by a fusion of metal, either by the low-temperature process of soft-soldering or the high-temperature process of silver-soldering, known also as hard-soldering. Movable joints are usually made by a process of hinging.

7. FINISHING AND POLISHING PROCESSES

Among these are the methods of finishing edges:—

(*a*) Folded Edges. An edge of metal is folded over itself, forming a double metal-thickness with a rounded edge.

(*b*) Wired Edges. A wire is inserted and closed in a turned-over edge or groove.

(*c*) Applied Moulding. Either soft or silver-soldered.

The final preparation of the surfaces, polishing and possibly colouring are the remaining operations of constructional hammered metalwork.

TOOL CONTROL

In all hammer and mallet operations, precision in the control of the tool used should be acquired as early as possible. The aim should be to make the hammer or mallet do its job with the minimum expenditure of energy. For ease of working, the height of the work is important and, in general, the elbow should be pressed into the side, the hammer pivoting at the wrist with as little movement of the forearm as possible. The control by the other hand is equally important. It supports the work on the stake face at the correct angle and, in addition, rotates it evenly at a speed which will allow the work of one hammer or mallet blow to overlap the preceding one.

Practice in the hammer processes will create a co-ordination of mind and hands which will make the use of the tools almost automatic, leaving the worker free to concentrate upon the shape being produced rather than upon the control of each individual hammer blow.

POINTS OF CONTACT AND IMPACT

In the foregoing shaping processes and also in planishing, a very important consideration is the way in which the metal is supported in contact with the stake or block on which it is shaped and also the relative position of the point of impact of the hammer on the work.

The relation of these two factors is illustrated in Plate I for each main process by arrow-heads, the lower one being the point of contact, or support of the work on the stake and the upper one the point of impact of the hammer on the work. It will be noted that they are co-incident for external stretching (Fig. 5) and planishing (Fig. 4) and that, for the remaining processes, the point of impact is in front of (or in advance of) the point of contact. If this relationship is appreciated in the early stages of work in hammered metalwork, much of the difficulty of the shaping processes disappears.

CHAPTER II

THE WORKSHOP AND ITS EQUIPMENT

Requirements—The Workroom—Position—Lighting—Gas and Water Supply—Work-bench—Tool Equipment—Workshop Arrangement—Care of Equipment.

HAMMERED metalwork requires neither expensive nor elaborate apparatus. It makes, however, certain demands in the matter of tools and equipment which must be met if good work is to be produced. These, in comparison with other basic crafts, are by no means unreasonable and are concerned chiefly with the design of individual tools and workshop equipment generally.

To a craftsman, his tools are primarily his servants. They are the means of expressing his wishes and desires in the material of his craft.

It should be the aim of a beginner to become a master craftsman at the earliest moment, in the sense that his hands are trained to complete mastery over each tool so that it may perform unhesitatingly and accurately his every bidding.

As a wise master must of necessity consider his servants, it follows that a craftsman's interest in and care for his tools should be such as will enable them to serve him most efficiently. His ability to sense what is required of a particular tool and willingness to maintain it in that condition, determines to a large degree his skill in his craft.

At the outset, it is important that a nucleus of good (though not necessarily the most expensive) tools is acquired, to which others may be added as the need arises. The design and quality of each tool should be such as will survive the advancing skill of its owner and not have to be discarded later because of its failure to meet the requirements of the mature craftsman. In this way an equipment of tools in which may be placed the utmost confidence becomes gradually accumulated from the commencement of·work in the craft.

The workroom must also be the subject of careful thought with the object of utilizing existing facilities to the best advantage. A well-planned and conveniently fitted workroom is a source of continual joy to its user, and its orderliness and good arrangement are conducive to the formation of habits of system and method in the work of those fortunate enough to use such a room.

No plan can be suggested for its layout, as so much depends upon individual conditions, but the main features constituting a suitable work-room for hammered metalwork are indicated.

POSITION

Some processes of the craft are noisy, and if there is a choice of position, the one which causes least annoyance to those near should be chosen. The sound of a hammer used with a ringing stake or anvil, whilst being music to the ear of a craftsman may be very distressing to those perhaps not so enthusiastic.

LIGHTING

The ideal lighting arrangement is one which does not produce strong shadows. This is usually effected by the provision of top lighting in conjunction with side lighting from an unobstructed window, near which the work bench is placed.

GAS AND WATER SUPPLY

A $\frac{3}{4}$ inch gas service pipe should be provided to feed a large blowpipe, though a $\frac{1}{2}$ or $\frac{3}{8}$ inch will serve if the pressure is good and very large work is not undertaken. A $\frac{3}{8}$ inch gas pipe to a soldering-stove is also necessary. Running water to a large deep sink is very desirable, though not essential. A draining-board fitted to the sink makes a convenient support for work whilst being scoured. A tub, barrel or washing-copper which can be emptied periodically makes a substitute for a sink.

WORK-BENCH

Considerable latitude is possible in the choice of a bench, the main requirement being rigidity. It should have a 2 inch hardwood top of as large an area as convenient with 3 inch bearers and cross-braced legs. The height of the bench should bring the face of a stake, or the top of a hollowing or shaping block, to a convenient height for working when placed in the bench vice. A space on the bench near the vice should be reserved for a piece of thin felt on which hammers and other polished tools are kept during use. A small table is also convenient for drawing and setting-out.

Tool Equipment

A list of essential tools is included, though it should not be assumed that all are necessary before a commencement can be made, nor yet that the list represents finality.   They are grouped in their functional arrangement :—

Drawing

Half-imperial drawing-board, tee-square, 60 and 45 degree set-squares. Celluloid protractor. Dividers. Pencil compasses. 12 inch boxwood rule, graduated in $\frac{1}{8}$ths and $\frac{1}{16}$ths of an inch. Drawing-pins. Hard pencil. India rubber. Proportional dividers are extremely useful though not essential.

Measuring and Setting-out

12 inch steel rule, graduated in $\frac{1}{8}$ths and $\frac{1}{16}$ths of an inch.   4 inch engineer's try-square.   12 inch woodworker's try-square.   Steel scriber. Centre-punch. 8 inch wing-compasses (or spring-dividers). Outside calipers. Sliding bevel. Scribing-block and surface-plate. Imperial Standard wire gauge.

Vices and other Holding Tools

$4\frac{1}{2}$ inch leg or bench vice rigidly bolted to the bench.   2 inch hand vice.   5 inch flat-nosed cutting pliers.   5 inch round-nosed pliers. Brass pickle tongs.   Small close-mouth, hollow-bit blacksmith's tongs.   Corn-tongs.   Sliding tongs or pin-vice.   Folding-bars.

Files

10 inch, second cut, flat, safe-edged.
10 inch, smooth, flat, safe-edged.
6 inch, second cut, flat, safe-edged.
6 inch, smooth, flat, safe-edged.
6 inch, smooth, half-round.
6 inch, smooth, triangular.
8 inch, smooth, round.
8 inch, smooth, square.
4 inch, smooth, warding.
4 inch, dead smooth, knife-edge.
Swiss files—assorted.

SHEARS

10 inch, straight shears.
8 inch, curved shears.
Scotch shears.

SAWS

8 inch Hacksaw frame—24-teeth-to-inch blades.
9 inch Jeweller's brass-back saw.
Piercing saw-frame and medium, round-backed blades.

DRILLS

Hand-drill (chuck to take $\frac{1}{4}$ inch drill).
Twist drills from $\frac{1}{4}$ to $\frac{1}{32}$ inch in sixty-fourths.

SCREWING EQUIPMENT

British Association stock and dies, taps and wrench, sizes 0, 2, 4 and 6.

DRAWPLATES

Circular, square and rectangular.

SOLDERING EQUIPMENT

Soft-soldering stove ($\frac{3}{8}$ inch gas service) screwed to a bench or table covered with sheet iron.
Square-pointed soldering-bit (12 oz.).
Silver-soldering hearth, with revolving tray.   Borax tray.
Whole, half and broken firebricks.
Blowpipe ($\frac{3}{4}$, $\frac{1}{2}$ or $\frac{3}{8}$ inch gas service).
Double-acting foot-bellows to suit the blowpipe in use, and fixed rigidly to the workroom floor.
Light rubber tubing for blowpipe connections.

SHAPING EQUIPMENT

10 inch or 8 inch leather sand-pad.
Various hardwood hollowing and sinking blocks.

MALLETS

Large and small flat mallets, rawhide or boxwood.
Doming mallet, boxwood.
Raising mallet, boxwood.

HAMMERS

Bench Hammers .	Engineer's (2 lb.)
	Warrington, Nos. 1 or 2 (6 or 8 oz.)
Hollowing Hammers.	Large, double-ended with curvatures of large radii (up to $2\frac{1}{2}$ lb.)
	Small, double-ended. Curvatures spherical or of small radii (12 oz.)
Sinking Hammers .	Large and small, double-ended with varying curvatures (2 lb. and 12 oz.)
Stretching Hammer .	Medium, double-ended with curvatures of large radii (1 lb.)
Collet Hammer .	Small, double-ended with curvatures of large radii (12 oz.)
Raising Hammer .	Small, double-ended. Flat faces $1\frac{1}{4} \times \frac{3}{8}$ in. and $1 \times \frac{3}{16}$ in. (12 oz.)
Planishing Hammers.	Large and small, double-ended, convex and flat (1 lb. and 6 oz.)
Chasing Hammer .	Small, flat (4 oz.)

STAKES

Bick-irons . .	Large, with long tapered beak (20 lb.)
	Small, with long tapered beak (10 lb.)
	Round, with long tapered beak (10 lb.)
Funnel Stake . .	Large (15 lb.) or Cone Mandrel.
Side Stake . .	Large (15 lb.) or round, parallel Mandrel.
Raising Stake . .	Large, two-arm, with curvatures of large radii (20 lb.)
Bottom Stake . .	Large, with machined tapering side (15 lb.)
Canister Stake . .	Medium, with machined parallel side (5 lb.)
Flat Anvil . .	Small (3 lb.)
Dome Head . .	Large (12 lb.)
Mushroom Stake .	Medium (5 lb.)
Ball Stake . .	Large (10 lb.)

Horse and detachable planishing heads of varying shapes and curvatures. (Stakes with rounded faces should be machined and polished well below the horizontal centre-line.)

Flatting and chopping-block, consisting of a cast-iron or mild-steel block about 10 or 12 inches square or larger, and 1½ or 2 inches in thickness. One face is machined and polished and the block is mounted loosely in a wood frame screwed to a bench. It is inverted when used on its unmachined face as a chopping-block.

A good deal of latitude must be permissible in the choice of hammers and stakes. Owing to lack of standardization, no precise details regarding these very important tools can be given and for this information toolmakers' catalogues should be consulted. Sketches are given in Plates 2 and 3 of typically good shapes.

PICKLING EQUIPMENT

Two earthenware, glass or lead-lined wooden troughs are required for acid pickles. These troughs should be used, if possible, in the open air outside the workshop and they should have well-fitting non-metallic covers. A large receptacle for water should be kept near the troughs for rinsing work after pickling, so that drips of acid are not carried back to the workroom.

CLEANING EQUIPMENT

File card or stiff steel wire brush.
Fine brass wire scratch-brush.
Nail brush.
Bristle polishing brushes.
Chamois leather.

GENERAL WORKROOM ARRANGEMENT

The work-bench should naturally occupy the best position in the room from the point of view of lighting and accessibility. Racks containing tools should be arranged as near the bench as convenient. Cupboard and shelving accommodation is indispensable, also drawers for small tools, drawings, patterns, etc. Boxes should be provided in which scraps of each metal are kept separately.

The silver-soldering hearth should be placed in a well-ventilated position and not in a strong light. It is desirable that two soldering hearths are used, one for soft and the other for silver-soldering. By this means the two processes may be kept entirely separate. The smallest size of blowpipe (¼ inch) is suitable for the soft-soldering hearth.

Files are conveniently hung in slotted metal racks, supported under their ferrules.

Hammers in constant use may be arranged in slotted wood racks, supported under their heads so that their faces can easily be seen.

A convenient way of using the larger stakes is to mount them in heavy timber—a length of floor-joist, for instance, which can be arranged as a rigid low bench that will bring the stake faces to a correct height when the user is seated on a stool. They may be used in this position or taken to a vice as required.

THE CARE OF EQUIPMENT

Every precaution should be taken to guard against damp in a workroom. If it is dry, then much of the equipment may be fitted in suitable racks near the place where it will be used, without fear of rusting. Acid fumes must be excluded from a workroom, as otherwise the surfaces of polished tools will be damaged by rust.

Bench tops should be kept entirely free from nails and embedded metal which may damage work by scratching. The surface-plate and flatting-block are worthy of special care. These tools should only be used for their respective purposes and when not in use should be protected by wooden covers, the inside recesses of which are fitted with a piece of thin felt which is occasionally oiled.

Files must never be stored in a heap. They are bad neighbours and will quickly ruin each other. Their blades should not be allowed to become wet and frequent use of the wire brush or file-card is necessary.

Shears must be correctly sharpened and the rivet should be tight enough to keep the blades in close contact whilst permitting easy movement. The sharpening angle of these tools is from 75 to 80 degrees. The method consists of placing each blade in turn in the vice and ' drawfiling ' it with a slipstone and oil. If the edges are finished rough, as from an emery-wheel, an unpleasant rough margin is left on the work when the shears are used.

The joints of pliers, tongs and shears, also vice screws and the working parts of hand-drills and other tools should be periodically oiled.

Screwing equipment, drawplates, brass-back saws and all polished tools not in general use should be greased with petroleum jelly when stored.

An occasional application of dubbin will keep the leather of footbellows in good condition.

Hammer and stake faces demand more attention and care from the metal craftsman than all his other equipment combined. (Suggestions in this connection will be found in Chapter VI.) The working faces of these tools should always be greased when not in constant use. Heavy stakes must never be stored in contact with each other. If this happens, damage to the polished faces will result.

Hammers must have well-fitting shafts, very securely wedged. When fitting a new shaft, it should be cut vertically along the major axis of its elliptical end to the depth of the hammer head with a tenon-saw. It is tapered with a wood-chisel until it is a good fit in the base of the eye of the hammer head and then driven through the eye so that it projects $\frac{1}{8}$ inch. A glued hardwood wedge is driven into the cut in the shaft and the waste removed. A serrated iron wedge is finally driven in on the minor axis, the waste removed with a hacksaw and cleaned off with an old file.

Detachable planishing heads which are a loose fit in the horse may be tightened when in use, by having a narrow strip of thin scrap copper laid across the square hole in the horse and the head driven in with a mallet.

CHAPTER III

MATERIALS

Classification of Metals—Properties of Metals—Copper—Brass—Gilding-metal—Silver—Sheet Metal and Wire Gauge—Non-metallic Materials—Material Sizes—Sundries.

A CRAFTSMAN's equipment is incomplete without a knowledge of the chief properties of the materials of his craft. He should know its possibilities and limitations so that he may use it correctly and to the best advantage.

Metals are either used in their basic state, singly, such as Copper, or as combinations of two or more metals which are known as Alloys, of which Brass, Gilding-metal and Standard Silver are examples.

Metals are also classed under two headings: Ferrous—those containing iron and Non-ferrous—which do not contain iron in any appreciable quantity.

PROPERTIES OF METALS

The Hardness of a metal is its resistance to penetration.

Its Brittleness is its tendency to fracture under percussion.

A metal possesses Lustre, or its power of reflecting light—a property which depends upon its immunity, or otherwise, from the oxidizing action of the gases of the air, which would destroy its polish.

The Malleability of a metal is its capability of withstanding hammering or rolling without fracture.

If a metal can be extended lengthwise by a process of wire-drawing, it possesses Ductility.

The property of a metal which allows of its being stretched tensionally without fracture and which is dependent upon its cohesion, is termed Tenacity.

The Fusibility of a metal is the readiness with which it fuses or becomes molten when heated. (A Refractory metal is one which melts only at a high temperature.)

Elasticity in a metal is its tendency to assume its original shape after being moved from it.

Its Conductivity is its power to conduct heat and electricity.

COPPER

Copper is a basic metal of a rich red colour, extremely malleable, ductile and tenacious and in its annealed state is soft and amenable to all the processes of hammered metalwork. It is very rapidly hardened by hammering and shaping operations generally.

Copper is filed with difficulty on account of its tendency to clog the file and its tenacity makes the operations of sawing, drilling and screwing somewhat troublesome. A lubricant is often desirable in these cutting operations.

The softness of copper must be realized when work is silver-soldered in a final process and therefore left in an annealed state.

Copper and its alloys are responsive to the action of acids and for this reason cannot be used in the making of food-containers unless the insides are tinned, or the work silver-plated.

The smooth surface of sheet copper is an indication of its fitness for hammered work and a sample presenting a dull, matt surface is one to be avoided.

Cold-rolled annealed copper should be ordered, as its surface will then be good, and its softness obviates preliminary annealing.

BRASS

Brass is an alloy of copper and zinc in widely varying proportions. Its colour range is from a full to a very pale yellow, its copper content determining its depth of colour. It is malleable and ductile and can be shaped by hammering, though not so readily as copper. It may be easily filed, sawn, drilled and screwed and these operations should be performed without a lubricant.

Brass hardens rapidly by being shaped and should be frequently annealed. Its melting-point varies with its zinc content, being low in alloys containing a large proportion of this metal.

For general hammered work, a brass alloy containing 65 parts of copper and 35 parts of brass is suitable, though for raised work a 70–30 proportion is preferable. It should be ordered soft-rolled.

GILDING-METAL

This metal is a copper-zinc alloy of much higher copper content than brass, usually 83–17, and is the colour of gold. It is not so malleable as copper and is much harder in its annealed state, therefore more suitable for work which is silver-soldered in a final process.

Gilding-metal takes a brilliant polish which is soon affected by the atmosphere.

Its melting-point is high, so that it may be heated with comparative safety.

A residue of copper is frequently present on its surface and its edge should be scraped and inspected, to prevent its being mistaken for copper when cutting new material.   It should be ordered soft-rolled.

Silver

Pure, or fine silver is too soft for general work and a harder alloy of silver and copper known as Standard silver is used, consisting of 925 parts of fine silver and 75 parts of copper.   Silver takes a brilliant polish and it is but slightly affected by atmospheric gases which, in time, produce a tarnish that eventually turns black without corrosion.

Silver is malleable and a most delightful metal in which to execute hammered work, though its high cost precludes its common use.   Its toughness renders silver less responsive to shaping operations than copper. In addition, the care in working usually bestowed upon it, makes the hammer processes somewhat slower in silver than in the base metals.

Its melting-point is comparatively low and great care is required in all heating operations.

Sheet silver should be ordered as 'Standard silver for spinning.' It will then be supplied with a good surface and annealed.

Sheet Metal and Wire Gauge

There are many gauges by which sheet metal and wires are measured, each bearing little or no relation to each other   One in common use is the Imperial Standard Wire Gauge, usually written S.W.G. and is used for sheet metal and wires.   Its gauge-numbers increase as the material thickness lessens.   (No. 10 S.W.G. is approximately equal to $\frac{1}{8}$ inch and No. 16 S.W.G. is roughly $\frac{1}{16}$ inch.)

Non-metallic Materials

Ivory, also Ebony and several similar dark close-grained hardwoods, are used in the making of handles and knobs.   These materials may be turned or worked to shape with files.   Vulcanized fibre is sometimes used for handles.   It may be planed to thickness with a finely set steel plane and is cut to shape with a hacksaw and finished with coarse and fine files and emery-cloth. Ebonite and Erinoid are also used for the hand-turning or filing of knobs. They are rather brittle and take a high polish.

MATERIAL SIZES

It would be almost impossible to suggest all the sizes in which material may be obtained and used. There is, however, a certain range of sizes in each class of material in which occur the more common sizes in general use. The more important of these are given in fractions of an inch and the Standard Wire Gauge, as applicable and in descending order :—

SHEET METAL

18, 19, 20, 21, 22 S.W.G.

WIRES

10, 12, 14, 16, 18, 20, 22 S.W.G. Round.
$\frac{3}{16}$, $\frac{1}{8}$, $\frac{3}{32}$ Half-round.
$\frac{1}{4}$, $\frac{3}{16}$, $\frac{5}{32}$, $\frac{1}{8}$, $\frac{3}{32}$, $\frac{1}{16}$ Square.

MOULDINGS

$\frac{1}{4}$, $\frac{3}{16}$, $\frac{1}{8}$ Astragal.
$\frac{3}{8}$, $\frac{1}{4}$, $\frac{3}{16}$ Reeded.

STRIP OR TAPE

$\frac{1}{2} \times \frac{1}{4}$, $\frac{3}{8} \times \frac{1}{4}$, $\frac{1}{4} \times \frac{1}{4}$.
$\frac{3}{4} \times \frac{1}{8}$, $\frac{1}{2} \times \frac{1}{8}$, $\frac{3}{8} \times \frac{1}{8}$, $\frac{1}{4} \times \frac{1}{8}$, $\frac{3}{16} \times \frac{1}{8}$.
$\frac{1}{2} \times \frac{1}{16}$, $\frac{3}{8} \times \frac{1}{16}$, $\frac{1}{4} \times \frac{1}{16}$, $\frac{3}{16} \times \frac{1}{16}$, $\frac{1}{8} \times \frac{1}{16}$.

TUBE FOR HINGES

10, 12, 14 S.W.G. Heavy walled, Solid-drawn.

SILVER-SOLDER

16 and 20 S.W.G. Round or Square Wire, in hard and easy-running grades.

SOFT-SOLDER

Fine, in thin sticks.

BLACK VULCANIZED FIBRE

$\frac{5}{8}$, $\frac{9}{16}$, $\frac{1}{2}$, $\frac{7}{16}$ Sheet.

2

EBONITE

1, $\frac{7}{8}$, $\frac{3}{4}$ Round rod. $\frac{5}{8}$, $\frac{9}{16}$, $\frac{1}{2}$, $\frac{7}{16}$ Sheet.

SUNDRIES

The sundry materials generally required are listed:—
Soft iron binding wire, 18, 20, 22 and 24 S.W.G.
Borax (in cone form).
Jewellers' Rouge.
Iron Split-pins (2 × $\frac{1}{8}$ and 1 × $\frac{1}{8}$ inch).
Medium and fine emery-cloth and ooo or oooo emery-paper.
Crocus or Carborundum powder (fine).
Flour emery powder.
Metal polish (good quality silver-polish).
Pumice powder (fine).
Water-of-Ayr slipstone ($\frac{1}{4}$ inch square), mottled or spotted.
Commercial concentrated acids—Sulphuric, Nitric and Hydro-chloric.
Scrap Zinc and Lead.
Thin lubricating oil.
Petroleum Jelly.
Swedish Pitch.
Plaster of Paris.
Tallow (plumber's dips).
Sal-ammoniac (lump).
Cotton waste.
Old soft rag.
Chalk.
Sawdust for drying.

CHAPTER IV

DRAWING

The Necessity for Drawing—The Working Drawing—Freehand Sketches—Plane and Solid Geometry—Pattern Drawing.

CONSIDERATION is given in this chapter to the type of drawing necessary. Hammered metalwork is sometimes assailed because larger inaccuracies would appear to be tolerated than in other metal crafts. It is admitted that its measurements are not set out in thousandths of an inch and that a micrometer caliper is not included in a list of essential measuring equipment. There is, however, no reason why a fine limit should not be worked to.

The frequent large inaccuracies which are met with in practice may be due to a variety of causes, among them being the failure to make a full-sized drawing and from it to estimate and make the necessary allowances for shaping operations correctly. If, for instance, a seamed conical form is required of a particular size, it becomes necessary to determine by a drawing the size and shape of the flat sheet of metal which may be bent to the desired cone. If the finished conical form has a folded or wired edge, it is necessary to make a definite allowance for it when the pattern is made.

In the case of a bowl, a full-sized drawing must be made before the work can commence, so that the size of the original flat circle of metal can be determined with accuracy and also to enable a templet to be made. When work is designed, the necessity for a full-sized drawing becomes greater than ever in order that its final proportions may be appreciated.

If an example of hammered metalwork is commenced without a full-sized working drawing, a very severe handicap is imposed at the outset and any degree of accuracy attained will be a matter of good fortune.

In simple work, inaccuracy may not be so vital. An ash-tray can be as pleasant in appearance and will do its job equally well if it is an eighth of an inch larger or smaller than was originally intended. Very soon, however, the need will arise for the correct fitting and jointing of work containing several parts. If the commencing and finishing sizes of these cannot readily be determined from an accurate drawing, the final fitting will be made extremely difficult.

It is not intended to deal with the drawing method in detail but rather to state the minimum requirements in technical drawing and plane and solid geometry.

FULL-SIZED WORKING DRAWING

The ability to produce a simple full-sized drawing of an example of work in orthographic projection, i.e. plan and elevation, is necessary, using a drawing-board, tee-square, set-squares and hard pencil. The work may be conveniently executed on quarter-imperial cartridge paper. Curves which are parts of circles are drawn with pencil compasses. Other curves not under this heading may be drawn freehand, care being taken to plot their symmetry from a centre-line.

Sectional and half-sectional elevations should be used wherever possible, and in many instances they are necessary to indicate the arrangement of joints.

FREEHAND SKETCHES

This form of rough sketching is of use in the early stages of the design of a piece of work. A pleasing shape of good proportion is often arrived at in this way and should be translated to a full-sized drawing with proportional dividers.

PLANE AND SOLID GEOMETRY

A background of plane and solid geometry is very desirable. *Geometrical Drawing for Art Students*, by I. H. Morris (Longmans, Green & Co.) is recommended.

PATTERN DRAWING

Sufficient facility in surface-development is necessary in order to produce correct patterns for cylinders and frusta or lower parts of cones and pyramids.

Practical methods of producing the commonly required patterns are briefly indicated, without reference to associated theory.

INSCRIBED POLYGON (Plate 4, Fig. 1)

The enclosing circle of the required polygon is drawn. Its diameter is equally divided into as many parts as the polygon has faces. Arcs are drawn with the diameter as radius, and their intersection joined to the second division of the diameter and the line continued to the circumference, thus indicating the length of the side of the polygon which is set off round the circumference.

ELLIPSE (Plate 4, Fig. 2)

The trammel method is generally suitable. The major and minor axes are carefully set out, also a strip of thick paper on which is marked the major and minor semi-axes by means of arrow-heads. With the arrow-heads in contact with the axes of the required ellipse, points are marked off which, when joined, complete an adjacent quarter of the ellipse.

CURVED SIDED RECTANGULAR FORM (Plate 4, Fig. 3)

This pattern is occasionally required, for example, for the concave side of a rectangular casket or a rectangular lid having a large rounded edge. The elevation is drawn and the curved side equally divided. The lengths of the divisions are set out down a vertical centre line. The intersections of horizontal and vertical projectors, drawn from these divisions, produce points which are joined to determine the boundary of the developed curved side.

CYLINDER (Plate 4, Fig. 4)

The pattern for a cylindrical form is simply a calculated rectangle, the length of which is $3\frac{1}{7}$ times the cylinder diameter and its breadth, the vertical height of the cylinder. When an oblique truncation is required, the pattern must be obtained by surface-development. The elevation of the cylinder with its oblique truncation is drawn. Its half-plan is included and divided equally. These divisions are projected back to the elevation and to the oblique truncation. Twice the number of these divisions are set out along a horizontal base-line. Intersecting vertical and horizontal projectors produce the development of the oblique truncation.

REGULAR PYRAMID (Plate 5)

The elevation is drawn, the half-plan included and the development set out on the part circumference of a circle, the centre and radius of which are the apex and base corner of the elevation respectively. (It should be noted that there are two principal positions in which the elevation may be drawn, Figs. 1 and 2.)

CONE (Plate 5)

The required cone is drawn in elevation and half-plan, half of which is equally divided. Four times the number of divisions are set out on the part circumference of a circle, the centre and radius of which are the apex and base-corner respectively (Fig. 3.)

If an oblique truncation is required, then the whole of the half-plan is equally divided and the divisions projected back to the base and then to the apex in the elevation. The points of intersection of these projectors with the oblique truncation in elevation, are projected horizontally and become arcs of circles in the development. Twice the number of divisions of the half-plan are set out on the developed base-circle and joined to the apex. Intersection of the two sets of projectors produces points on a curve which determine the development of the oblique truncation (Fig. 4). In the case of a cone having only a very small taper, i.e. when the base angles are only slightly less than right-angles, it will be found impossible to make the development drawing with ordinary compasses, due to the large vertical height of the complete cone. The required truncated cone should be set out on a piece of cartridge paper pinned to the lower left-hand corner of a large drawing-board or table. The cone sides are continued to the apex and beam-compasses used to draw the arcs forming the development. If beam-compasses are not available, a drawing-pin should be inserted at the apex, over which is passed the looped end of a piece of thread or thin string. The free end is wrapped two or three times round a pencil near its point. The required arcs are then drawn, using the pencil vertically and with a fair tension on the thread.

CHAPTER V

ESTIMATING INITIAL DIMENSIONS AND ALLOWANCES

Reasons for Preliminary Estimation of Sizes—Hollowing—Low Hollowing—Raising—Folded Box—Splayed Surface—Stretched Cone—Contracted Cone—Multi-process Cone—Applied Moulding to a Spherical Surface—Wired Edge—Folded Edge—Folded Corners of Regular Polygons—Planishing.

THE effect of the shaping processes of hammered metalwork is to rearrange the material. In most cases they produce three-dimensional forms from two-dimensional material (if the thickness of sheet metal is neglected). The rearrangement is effected by tension or compression and shaping may take place merely by an alteration in the relative position of surfaces.

Whatever shaping process operates, the finished form bears little apparent relation to a flat sheet of metal from which the work must be commenced. When planning work which involves a major shaping process, it is necessary that the subsequent change in form is understood so that the initial dimensions or measurements of the flat material may be correctly estimated. The requirement is that the work shall commence from a piece of material of the correct shape, which contains just sufficient metal to be shaped to the desired form.

Some processes, e.g. Edge-wiring, require a further allowance of metal in addition to that required for the shaping process, which must be added to the original estimate when the work is commenced. Also it is often desirable to deliberately add a small excess of metal at the beginning, which will form a waste margin to simplify a jointing operation.

This estimation of initial dimensions and allowances should be regarded as a very important part of the craft upon which depends, to a large extent, the final accuracy.

The procedure is summarized, and it should be understood that until experience has been gained the methods are approximate only. They form, however, a basis for personal experiment, and it is wise to allow a little extra metal in the early stages, which may be removed when progress of the work has been noted. The allowances are not constant for all gauges of metal and variations are apparent with individual workers, so that, as ever, experience is the most valuable guide.

HOLLOWING (Plate 6, Fig. 1)

A line drawn from the centre to the top edge in the elevation drawing is the radius of the original circle of metal.

LOW HOLLOWING (Plate 6, Fig. 2)

To the diameter of the flat part of the base must be added twice the length of the chord of the arc which forms the side in the elevation drawing.

RAISING (Plate 6, Fig. 3)

This estimation can only be approximate, as several factors operate, though a rough guide for low forms is the maximum diameter added to the height as the diameter of the commencing circle. Taller forms will require less metal.

FOLDED BOX (Plate 6, Fig. 4)

The length of the required rectangle will be the length of the base plus twice the height, and the breadth will be the breadth of the base plus twice the height.

SPLAYED SURFACE (Plate 6, Fig. 5)

The pattern for a folded box or similar form with flat sloping sides must have the developed surface of each side added to the base. It will be realized that the front elevation of the sloping side is neither its true shape nor size. The slant height in elevation is the vertical height in the development, the length being constant.

STRETCHED CONE (Plate 6, Fig. 6)

The elevation of the cone from which a stretched seamed vase or similar form is commenced, must be determined from the working drawing. Consideration must be given to the amount of stretching which can take place before undue thinning is apparent. A slight increase in height should also be made in the estimation.

CONTRACTED CONE (Plate 6, Fig. 7)

This is another example of similar procedure in which a cone is estimated which can be contracted to a form having a concave profile.

MULTI-PROCESS CONE (Plate 6, Fig. 8)

The two foregoing processes are often interchangeable in the shaping of seamed work. The stretched cone, for instance, could be contracted from a larger cone and the contracted cone could be stretched from a smaller one. In this type of shaping, the ease of working and also the thinning of the metal will decide the method used. A common procedure is to execute the work by more than one process. The example given is a seamed bowl-mounting, shaped in three operations. The centre is contracted and the top and base internally stretched and finally the edges are turned. In this case the side of the elevation of the estimated cone is a line which is a mean of the final curve, allowances for the turned edges being added to the height.

APPLIED MOULDING TO A SPHERICAL SURFACE (Plate 6, Fig. 9)

When a flat moulding is applied to a bowl rim which is not vertical, it must be bent in two directions. The inner flat surface must be inclined to fit the slope of the bowl (in elevation) and it must also be bent to a circle to fit the rim (in plan). If this double bending is attempted in one operation it will be extremely difficult to get a good fit. A moment's consideration will show that the finished circle of moulding may be regarded as a cone so far as its inner surface is concerned. It is therefore possible to develop it before it is applied, by bending it in the flat to a circle of a predetermined radius.

The full-sized elevation of the bowl is drawn and the moulding included in its required position. The inner faces of the moulding are produced as straight lines to their intersection, which is used as a centre for two circles, the radii of which extends to the upper and lower edge of the moulding respectively.

The required length of moulding is now bent in the flat and fitted accurately between these development curves. When bent to fit the bowl in the application process, it will automatically assume the slope of the bowl rim.

WIRED EDGE (Plate 6, Fig. 10)

The extra metal required to form a wired edge is termed the wiring-allowance and it is necessary that its estimation is accurate. If too much is allowed, it will be impossible to close the edge correctly, whilst the wire will remain exposed if too little is included. To ensure accuracy it is a wise plan to enclose a short length of the wire to be used in a strip of the required gauge of sheet metal about $\frac{1}{4}$ inch wide, before commencing the wiring operation. The strip is marked with a scriber, which is held at an angle of 45 degrees on the side remote from the turned-in edge of the strip. The wire is removed and the strip opened and flatted with a mallet. From the scriber mark to the end will be the wiring-allowance for that particular gauge of sheet metal and wire, provided that no stretching of the wiring-allowance takes place during the turning and closing operations.

FOLDED EDGE (Plate 6, Fig. 11)

The folding allowance is equal to the width of the completed folded edge. The fact that the fold is left rounded and will therefore require slightly more metal need not be allowed for, unless very fine limits are being worked to.

FOLDED CORNERS OF REGULAR POLYGONS (Plate 6, Fig. 12)

When folding the edges of regular polygons, it becomes necessary to remove the waste corner before the folding is commenced. The polygon, plus its folding allowance, is cut to size. A bevel is set and with it the corners are set out from their adjacent edges. The angle to which the bevel is set is found by the formula $90 + \dfrac{180}{n}$, where n is the number of sides of the polygon.

PLANISHING

A small allowance must frequently be made for the slight stretching due to planishing, the exact amount varying with each job. As an example, the elevation drawing of the hexagonal pyramid required for the cream jug (Plate 63) should be $\frac{1}{16}$ inch less than the required finished width. (This type of allowance may be neglected in elementary work.)

CHAPTER VI

PREPARATION AND CARE OF METAL SURFACES

Removal of Large Blemishes—Annealing—Pickling—Scouring—Flatting—Removal of Small Blemishes—Care of Metal Surfaces during Working—Use of Emery-cloth—Summary.

MUCH of the character of hand craftsmanship in hammered silver and the base metals lies in the beauty of a carefully finished surface, whether it be the lustre of its polished smoothness, or the charm of a finely hammered texture, reflecting the light from a myriad tiny facets.

At the commencement of even the simplest work in the craft it is wise to realize the importance of the processes which initially prepare the surface of the metal, and during its working to consider the method by which it is maintained in the condition so necessary for the production of the careful finish and restrained polish which characterize good handwork in metal.

Metal cut from the sheet is seldom in a fit condition for working. Its surface may be scratched and pitted, or even blistered. It will probably be hard and springy and anything but flat.

REMOVAL OF LARGE BLEMISHES

Both faces must be examined for blisters and faults in the metal due to its having been rolled from an imperfect ingot. These are fortunately rare, but should blisters be discovered it is safer to discard the particular piece of metal. Blisters may be occasionally removed by filing and scraping, but they frequently reappear during a shaping process, and if on the inside of a form, are particularly difficult to remove.

Long, straight scratches should be removed with a smooth file, the metal having been bent over the edge of the bench along the line of the scratch, to raise it above the surrounding surface.

Pitted blemishes are treated in the same way, except that they are slightly raised by being struck on the reverse side with a doming mallet, the metal resting on a sand-pad.

The file marks are removed with coarse and fine emery-cloth. There is, of course, a limit to the filing operation in the removal of a blemish, due to its thinning effect. If taken to excess, a serious depression will result when the metal is flatted.

ANNEALING

To make subsequent shaping processes as easy as possible the metal must be soft, or in an annealed state. Also, during working, metal rapidly hardens and acquires stresses and strains which make it springy and unyielding. When this condition is reached, annealing becomes necessary to render it once more easily workable.

The process consists of raising the temperature of the metal to a very dull red heat and either quenching it in water or cooling in air, depending upon the particular metal in use.

The sheet should be placed flat on the soldering-hearth supported on small pieces of broken fire-brick, asbestos or pumice so that heat is not lost by conduction to the soldering-hearth. It should also be surrounded by whole or half fire-bricks to prevent loss of heat by radiation (Plate 7, Fig. 1).

A large blowpipe flame is directed on to the metal at right-angles to its surface at a sufficient height from the work to produce the hottest flame.

When the work becomes a very dull red it is sufficiently annealed and further heating will not appreciably increase its softness.

Copper and Gilding-metal may be quenched in cold water or left to cool in air.

Silver may twist or become distorted if suddenly quenched.

Brass, unless of good quality, i.e. having a high copper content, may develop small cracks if quenched, therefore it is safer to cool it slowly. In any case brass should not be handled with tongs at red heat, as some grades become brittle and liable to fracture in that state. Great care is required in heating brass on account of its relatively low melting-point. Low-grade brass may fuse before red heat is attained.

Certain general precautions are necessary in annealing :—

Local heating should be avoided. The whole of the job should be heated evenly and slowly to prevent unequal expansion.

Work containing soft-soldered joints cannot be annealed. The temperature at which the metal is annealed is far above the fusing-point of soft-solder. Also it is very necessary to ensure that no traces of soft-solder come in contact with work at red heat. Soft-solder will bite into, and sometimes completely through, sheet silver, copper, etc., when these metals are at red heat.

Work that has been previously silver-soldered must be annealed with care and never heated to more than a dull-red heat, otherwise the joints may fuse and become displaced.

A job containing several parts silver-soldered together should not be quenched at red heat after annealing. Distortion caused by uneven contraction may occur, which is not easily corrected.

The annealing of wires requires great care, and in every case wire should be coiled into a hank and the strands wrapped together by the ends of the hank. It is then gradually heated by a large soft flame (Plate 7, Fig. 2). If the process is unduly hurried, individual strands of wire will take excessive heat and may be rapidly fused.

PICKLING

After the annealing process, the metal will be covered with oxide and scale and must be pickled, i.e. immersed in an acid solution to remove the oxide and other impurities from its surfaces.

A suitable cleaning pickle for copper, gilding-metal and brass is ‘ Commercial Concentrated ’ Sulphuric Acid in from 5 to 10 volumes of water used in a lead-lined, earthenware or glass trough (Plate 7, Fig. 3). A few minutes’ immersion in this solution is required, the time depending on the strength of the pickle. The work should then be washed very thoroughly in running water.

Extreme care is required in the handling of acid pickles and steps must be taken to prevent splashing.

Non-ferrous tongs must be used to handle work in a pickle-bath and iron in any form must not be introduced into the solution. If this happens, copper may be deposited on subsequent work in gilding-metal and brass.

When making up a pickle bath it is important that the acid is added to the cold water very slowly, to prevent overheating of the solution. If the water is poured over the concentrated acid, the resulting action is often sufficiently violent to throw the acid out of the trough.

Silver must be ‘ boiled-out ’ in a copper pan containing a pickle of sulphuric acid in 10 volumes of water. A bunsen burner or gas-ring is used for heating.

Work in gilding-metal and brass often shows an unpleasant coppery coloration. This may be due to one of three causes. When these metals are heated, zinc (a constituent of the alloys) is volatilized from the surface, leaving a copper residue. The work may have been immersed in a pickle into which iron has been introduced, or the pickle may have attacked the zinc on the metal surface, leaving a patchy coloration. In either case, a cleaning pickle will not remove the coloration and a solution of equal parts of concentrated Nitric and Sulphuric acids in from 5 to 10 volumes of water is necessary. This latter is quite a serviceable pickle for general use, though it must be realized that it is something more than a cleaning agent. If work is left in a pickle containing Nitric acid longer than is required for cleaning or the removal of copper residue, the surface of the work will be matted or made dull and perhaps pitted.

Care is also required in pickling work containing soft-soldered joints. It should be pickled before the joints are cleaned off, as the soft-solder may be disintegrated by the acid, producing what appear to be undercut joints. Actually they have been ' eaten back ' by the action of the acid.

It is possible to make up many acid dips for special purposes, notably those termed ' satin ' and ' bright ' dips, which produce a satin (or matt) surface or a bright finish simply by dipping the work. For the type of metalwork under consideration, they should be avoided, as their action is too violent to allow of easy regulation and their use often results in seriously damaged surfaces. Occasionally, it is very convenient to use a strong acid for cleaning a part of a job quickly. A piece of rag tied to a stick and dipped in concentrated Nitric acid and applied to the work will have an instant effect. The operation should be performed near running water so that the work may be quickly rinsed.

SCOURING

When work has been washed in running water after pickling, the surface usually requires scouring with pumice-powder and water used on a nail-brush, after which it may be rinsed and dried in a box containing fine hot sawdust, or it may be placed on the soldering-hearth and dried by passing a large soft flame over its surface.

FLATTING

After scouring, the metal is ready for flatting, which is most conveniently done on a cast-iron flatting-block, having a brightly polished surface and free from blemishes in the metal, and grit, rust or grease on the surface. A rawhide or wooden mallet is used, the face of which is very slightly convex, the corners being still further rounded off.

The high places in the metal are malleted down on to the block on one side, then the metal is reversed and the same process carried out on the other side until the whole of the surface is evenly in contact with the block (Plate 7, Fig. 4).

The mallet faces should be free from tiny pieces of embedded metal which would scratch and pit the surface of the work. If the surface of the flatting-block is in poor condition, then a sheet of paper should be placed over the block when flatting.

Removing Small Blemishes

The surfaces should now be again inspected for smaller blemishes, which may be removed with a scraper used lightly with both hands, the scraper crossing the blemish in oblique strokes (Plate 7, Fig. 5).

Scraper marks and other tiny defects are now removed by a light rubbing with Water-of-Ayr stone and water in a circular motion, finally rinsing in running water and drying off (Plate 7, Fig. 6).

Surfaces are also ground with Water-of-Ayr stone and water when it is desired to remove facets made by planishing or other hammer processes.

Care of Metal Surfaces during Working

Much of the time spent in the initial preparation will have been wasted if attention is not given to the preservation of good surfaces during the subsequent processes.

Work carelessly handled will accumulate minor defects and tiny blemishes on its surfaces which pass unnoticed unless it is frequently inspected. If these are allowed to remain until the final cleaning-up, any polishing process will merely accentuate them. If they are then removed with files, scrapers and emery-cloth it will be found that the surrounding hammered surfaces have been seriously impaired.

Scratches and other blemishes should be prevented by careful handling, though accidents frequently happen, especially in the early stages. A file slips from an edge, grit is picked up on a hammer face, a tool is handled carelessly and perhaps excess solder is applied to a joint, all leaving some slight blemish on the metal. If these are removed as soon as they appear, less harm is done to the work and the final surface-preparation is bound to be more successful.

Certain precautions during working are necessary. It is absolutely essential that every tool which comes in contact with a metal surface shall be itself free from blemishes and also that its working faces are highly polished. Defects on a hammer or stake face are transferred to the work with every hammer blow.

Sharp edges on tools will produce bruises and scars on the work which are often impossible to remove. All corners and sharp edges must be carefully rounded off and the working faces polished bright.

A piece of thin leather, about 10 inches long and 2 inches wide, glued with its rough side uppermost to a piece of wood and sprinkled with flour emery-powder, should be kept on the bench for polishing hammer faces by rubbing them on its surface. It is used in the same way as a file would be held, to polish stake faces.

Considerable damage may be caused by the serrated inner faces of vice jaws. Whenever work is held in a vice it must be protected by vice clams or angle pieces of sheet lead or soft copper (Plate 33, Fig. 2). Thin cardboard should be used in addition to protect the surfaces of polished work.

A work-bench should be kept clear of all unwanted tools and its surface should be frequently inspected for tiny pieces of embedded metal and grit.

When binding-wire is used in soldering operations it must not be allowed to scratch the surface of the work nor yet cut into finished edges.

Care is also needed in the handling of hot metal with tongs and in moving it on the soldering-hearth so that its surface is not scratched by fire-bricks. It is necessary that all traces of fused borax are removed, by pickling, from work which requires subsequent hammering. If this precaution is neglected, the surfaces will be badly pitted when the fused borax is finally cleaned off.

Use of Emery-cloth and Emery-paper

Emery-cloth should be regarded as a tool having a well-defined usage. The surfaces of hammered work may be hopelessly ruined by its incorrect use.

Coarse and medium emery-cloth are necessary in the finishing of steel and iron tools and for the removal of small blemishes in stake faces. On no account should they be used on the soft metals in constructional work, other than to follow a file or scraper in the preliminary surface preparation. They should precede the use of Water-of-Ayr stone and water.

Fine emery-cloth is used in the cleaning-off of wired and folded edges, mouldings and soft and silver-soldered joints. Whenever possible it should be used on small lengths of wood which have been planed to a square or bevelled edge. Its most effective use is when it is glued to these wood edges. Use on the thumb is only justified when finishing rounded edges and if used in this way elsewhere it will speedily destroy the good appearance of corners. Fine emery-cloth must never be used on a hammered surface.

Emery-paper, ooo or oooo, is used in the same way when a finer surface is required than can be obtained with fine emery-cloth. (Its restrained use on a hammered surface is sometimes permissible.)

If a smooth untooled surface is required, emery-cloth can take its place with any other coarse abrasive in the final surface-preparation.

If, however, a finely and evenly hammered texture is aimed at, it must be realized that if emery-cloth is used at any time, the surface will be impaired. After even a light rubbing the surface will still be a hammered one, but it will have lost its character and will appear lifeless and uninteresting. The reason is that emery-cloth produces uneven wear on such a surface. On a curving hammered surface each tiny facet is an independent flat plane and on a flat hammered surface each tool-impression will have an almost imperceptible concavity. Emery-cloth, being of necessity stiff and unyielding, will remove metal from the edges of each facet or tool-impression and will not reach the centres, producing in time an isolated, pitted appearance. Conversely, a fine abrasive in powder form used with a thin oil on soft rag will produce more even wear. (The foregoing notes would probably be more applicable in the chapter on polishing. They are included here as it is realized that a temptation is present to use emery-cloth in the early stages of a job, and if a hammered surface has once been damaged by emery-cloth no attention at a later stage can restore it.)

SUMMARY OF PROCEDURE

    (a) *Initial Preparation of Surfaces*
        Inspection—and removal of large blemishes.
        Annealing.
        Pickling.
        Scouring.
        Flatting.
        Removal of small blemishes.

(b) *Care of Metal Surfaces during Working*

Pickling.

Scouring.

Extreme care in handling—and the removal of small blemishes as they occur.

It must not be thought that the foregoing processes involve much irksome labour or that they entail the spending of a great deal of time. They do not. Rather should they be regarded in the light of a necessary routine, very soon becoming almost automatic, and which is amply repaid by the excellence of the finish.

It is the attention to details such as these that distinguishes a craftsman from a workman.

CHAPTER VII

SETTING-OUT

Definition—Requirements—Straight Lines—Circles and Arcs—Narrow Parallel Strip—Rectangles—A Hexagon—An Octagon—Other Regular Polygons—Finding the Centre of a Circle—Curves not Parts of Circles—Centres of Drilled Holes—An External Height-line—An Internal Height-line—Bowl Mountings and Similar Forms—Guide Lines.

IN some of the stages through which an example of hammered metalwork passes in its progress from the flat sheet, the necessity arises for lines to be drawn on the surfaces of the work. They may indicate the commencing size and shape of the metal as the first cutting lines. They may determine the final form of the work as folding or bending lines. Others may define the limits of a particular process, acting merely as temporary guide lines, or they may mark the waste metal at the completion of the work as final cutting lines.

These lines, the object of which is to guide the worker at each stage, are termed the setting-out, and upon its correct application and accuracy depend the successful interpretation of the design in terms of metal.

The fact that no trace of these constructional lines must appear on finished work, decides, to a great extent, their form. The most accurate line on a metal surface is undoubtedly one cut with a fine steel point called a scriber. If it is in a position where it can be removed in the construction, as in the case of cutting and folding lines, it is then the correct one to use.

In other cases where a cut line cannot be removed without damage to the surrounding metal texture, then a hard pencil must be relied upon.

A safe rule is: Cutting and folding lines set out with a scriber—all others with a hard pencil.

STRAIGHT LINES are set out with a steel rule or straight-edge, and lines at right-angles to an edge with a try-square, whilst those at other angles are applied by means of a bevel.

CIRCLES AND ARCS are struck with either wing-compasses or spring-dividers. It is very frequently necessary to inscribe a circle in a square of metal.   The diagonals of the square should be drawn in pencil and their intersection used as a centre for the circle.   The pivot-leg of the compasses will make a centre-dot which is sometimes very difficult to remove.   To avoid this difficulty a loose centre should be used.   It consists of a slightly hollowed disc the size of a shilling.   The lower edge is ground flat whilst the convex side has two lines intersecting at right-angles scribed upon it, the intersection of the lines being centred with a centre punch.   In use it is placed over the pencil diagonals on the metal and held in position whilst its centre is used for the pivot-leg of the compasses, thus obviating any mark on the metal (Plate 8, Fig. 1).   The disc should not have any appreciable height, as an error would in that case be introduced in the radius of the circle.

NARROW PARALLEL STRIP may be set out from a face-edge of metal previously trued up by setting wing-compasses to the desired width of the strip.   With the metal on a flat surface, one leg of the compasses marks the metal, the other sliding against the face-edge (Plate 8, Fig. 2). (Hermaphrodite calipers may be used if available.)

RECTANGLES are set out from a previously trued-up face-edge.   Two lines, the length of the rectangle apart are squared across the metal with a try-square (Plate 8, Fig. 3).   A measurement equal to the breadth of the rectangle is set off along each of the squared lines.   The two points are then joined with a straight-edge.

A HEXAGON is inscribed in a circle, the diameter of which equals the measurement of the hexagon across the corners.   The radius of the circle is stepped round its circumference from opposite ends of a diameter, with spring-dividers and the points joined (Plate 8, Fig. 4).   (It should be noted that this method is only applicable to flat metal and cannot be used on a domed surface.)

AN OCTAGON is inscribed in a square, the side of which equals the measurement of the octagon across its sides.   Using the corners of the square as centres, points are marked off on the adjacent sides, with half the diagonal as radius.   The points are joined with a straight-edge to complete the octagon (Plate 8, Fig. 6).

OTHER REGULAR POLYGONS are inscribed in circles by trial and error, stepping-off points round the circumference with spring-dividers which have been set to the length of the side of the figure, obtained from a previously made drawing on paper (Plate 4, Fig. 1).

Finding the Centre of a Circle

Intersecting arcs are struck from four points on the circumference which are roughly 90 degrees apart. The centre of the circle will be the intersection of the diagonals of the small rectangle formed by the intersecting arcs (Plate 8, Fig. 5).

Curves not Parts of Circles should be marked off from a templet or pattern made in tinplate or other thin sheet metal. Curves should never be drawn freehand on metal.

Centres of Drilled Holes are indicated by a lightly struck centre-dot made with a centre-punch and hammer, the work being supported on a metal block. A centre-punch should never be used on sheet metal for any purpose other than that of marking the centre of a drilled hole.

An External Height-line is applied to the outside of a form by means of a scribing-block on a surface-plate. The scribing-block is set to the required height, the work and block being pressed on to the surface-plate, whilst the line is being marked (Plate 8, Fig. 7).

An Internal Height-line is set out on the inside of a form, as in the case of the external height-line, except that it is usually more convenient to use the curved end of the scribing-block needle, which is set at a suitable angle (Plate 8, Fig. 8).

False Centres for Bowl Mountings and Similar Forms

When a bowl-mounting has been raised from the flat sheet, or shaped from a seamed cone, it becomes necessary to set out a circle near each edge on its inner surface to indicate the waste for the purpose of truing and cleaning off the edges. When the final shaping is finished, no centre exists. A temporary false centre, from which to strike the circles, must therefore be provided by fitting a piece of wood reasonably tightly in the internal diameter of the work on which the accurate centre for the circle is set out (Plate 8, Fig. 5).

Guide Lines

Accuracy in the shaping processes is facilitated if guide lines are applied to the work before commencing. They usually consist of concentric pencil circles from $\frac{1}{4}$ to $\frac{1}{2}$ inch apart. In the early stages of a shaping process, light cut lines with a spring-divider may be used, if preferred. If they are made with heavy pressure or used near the completion of the process, their removal will be the cause of a good deal of trouble.

Lines which mark the limit of a particular operation may be used with advantage in the same way.

CHAPTER VIII

CUTTING PROCESSES

General Considerations—Use of Shears—Straight Cuts—External Curves—Internal Curves—Thin Strips and Flat Mouldings—Waste Margin—Surplus Vertical Edges—Wire—Thick Strips and Heavy Mouldings—Mitring—Saw-piercing—Parting—Drilling—Hand Screwcutting.

As sheet metal forms the basic material of hammered metalwork, it follows that the correct methods of cutting it are of great importance. Considerable use is made of wires, thin strips and mouldings and, to a much less extent, non-metallic material, e.g. ebony, ebonite, ivory and black fibre, in the construction of handles and knobs. In whatever form the material may be, there are certain methods of cutting which are more efficient than the rest.

At first sight these may appear slower than others that could be suggested, but very often much time is saved, as the cut is nearer to a finished surface than would otherwise be possible.

An important fact which should never be lost sight of is that in only a few cases can a cut be made which is in an absolutely finished condition. Frequently, a further operation is necessary which results in a loss of material. If this slight loss is not allowed for when the cut is made, the work will finish under size when cleaned off.

A cut must not be made directly on the line, but on the waste side of it and at a sufficient distance away to allow of a tiny margin for cleaning off to remain. If this waste margin is too wide, much time will be lost in the cleaning-off process before the line is reached. The most efficient cutting method, therefore, is the one which leaves only just sufficient waste metal to enable the rough and uneven surface to be removed.

USE OF SHEARS

For the ordinary cutting of sheet metal, hand shears are used, convenient sizes being 10 inch straight and 8 inch curved. Shears may be either right or left handed, and a ' universal ' pattern may be obtained in either ' hand,' which can be used for straight cutting or internal curves.   Shears should be gripped near the ends of the handles, with the first finger between them.   The blades are closed by a steady grip of the hand and opened with the first finger.

Care should be taken to ensure that when the ends of the handles close they are clear of the flesh on the inside of the hand.

Shears should never be gripped with both hands.   One hand must always hold and guide the work, and if the metal is too thick for easy, steady cutting, then one handle may be held in a vice and the cut made by a downward pressure on the loose handle.

Shear blades should not be allowed completely to close during a long cut, as this will produce unpleasant notches along the cut edge.

The inner flat surface of the upper blade must always be kept at a right-angle to the metal being cut, thus preventing a distorted margin to the cut edge.

Thick sheet metal should be cut with Scotch shears, which are a large heavy pattern and are always used in a vice.

STRAIGHT CUTS are made with straight shears (Plate 9, Fig. 1).

EXTERNAL CURVES are cut with straight shears.   If a circle is being cut from a square, the cutting is made easier if the waste corners are first removed by straight cuts at 45 degrees (Plate 9, Fig. 2).

INTERNAL CURVES are cut with curved shears (Plate 9, Fig. 3).

THIN STRIPS AND FLAT MOULDINGS in the smaller sizes may be cut with straight shears.   The projecting waste ends of circles in thin, narrow material are cut in one operation (Plate 9, Fig. 4).

A WASTE MARGIN should always be removed with curved shears, as the cutting edge is then only in contact with the metal at one point, which minimizes distortion of the work (Plate 9, Fig. 5).

SURPLUS VERTICAL EDGES are also cut with curved shears to an inside height-line whenever possible.   By this method the line remains visible during the operation (Plate 9, Fig. 6).

WIRE of medium gauge is cut with side-cutting pliers (Plate 10, Fig. 1).   Thin wires can easily be cut with shears, and heavy gauges are sawn with either a hacksaw, brass-back saw or piercing-saw.

THICK STRIPS AND HEAVY MOULDINGS must be cut in a vice with a hacksaw or brass-back saw (Plate 10, Figs. 2, 3 and 4).

RINGS OF WIRE are formed by coiling on a round bar or parallel mandrel and then cutting in the vice with a brass-back saw (Plate 10, Fig. 5).

MITRING of wires and mouldings is executed in a small hardwood mitre-block in a vice, using a brass-back saw (Plate 10, Fig. 6). The rebate in the mitre-block may be worked with a rebate plane or it may be formed by screwing a smaller piece of wood to the block. When numbers of pieces of moulding of equal length are to be mitred, for example, in the application of an edge moulding to a tray, the rim of which is a regular polygon, the following procedure will be found to be an accurate method of cutting.

A bevel is set to the mitre angle from the formula $90 - \dfrac{180}{n}$, where n is the number of sides of the polygon.

A cut is made in the mitre-block with the brass-back saw, to this angle. The required length of the pieces of moulding is set out with spring-dividers from the first cut, along the internal angle of the rebate, and the second cut made in the mitre-block.

Lengths of moulding, having a small waste allowance, are prepared and flatted, and one end of each mitred. A small piece of tinplate or thin sheet metal is placed in the mitre cut in the block which has already been used. The mitred end of each piece of moulding is pushed up against the tinplate stop and the remaining end mitred in the second cut. This method ensures that each piece of moulding is of identical length, a condition absolutely necessary in the building up of a regular polygon of wire, strip or moulding.

SAW-PIERCING

Large circular holes and irregular closed voids are usually cut with a piercing-saw on a piercing-board (or V-table) screwed to the bench (Plate 11, Fig. 1). The saw-blade is inserted in one end of the frame with the teeth pointing downwards and a small drilled hole is required to form an entry for the saw-blade, which is then passed through the hole in the work and clamped in the saw-frame with a reasonable tension.

The cutting takes place on the down stroke, the work being turned on the piercing-board to follow the required curve. The direction of the cut should be always forwards, away from the worker, with the saw-blade at a right-angle to the face of the metal being cut.

Chopping-out

The same work may be performed by another process—that of Chopping-out (Plate 11, Fig. 2). Holes are drilled inside the set-out curve and the ties or bridges of metal between the holes are then cut through with a small thin chisel, the work being supported on a chopping-block. (On no account must a flatting-block or surface-plate be used.) The first method (saw-piercing) should be used whenever possible. Chopping-out requires a good deal of cleaning off and distortion frequently occurs.

Parting is the name given to the cutting process which separates a sheet-metal form into two parts, usually for the purpose of detaching a lid (Plate 11, Fig. 3).

A piece of wood is cut which is a tight fit inside the work and held in the vice by its projecting thickness. If the work already has a base fitted, then a second piece of wood must be provided to protect the base. The cut is made with a brass-back saw, the work being rotated in the vice as required.

Drilling

A small hand-drill of $\frac{1}{4}$ inch capacity and twist drills may be used either vertically or horizontally for the drilling of small holes in thick material held in a vice (Plate 11, Fig. 4). Sheet metal may be drilled, supported horizontally on a woodworker's sawing-board.

Hand Screwcutting

These processes are required in the making of bolts for the fitting of knobs.

Screwing

An external thread is cut on the shank of a bolt or screw by a die which is held in a stock. The rod to be screwed is slightly pointed and held vertically in a vice and the die screwed down it to the required depth (Plate 11, Fig. 6).

TAPPING

An internal thread in a hole is cut by a process of tapping, with a tap held vertically in a tap-wrench (Plate 11, Fig. 5). A taper tap is used to commence the thread and is followed by a plug (or parallel) tap which continues the thread to the correct depth.

Convenient sizes for screw threads for the work under consideration may be selected from British Association Nos. 0, 2, 4 and 6. There are three important dimensions concerned :—

1. *Diameter*
The full diameter of the finished screw (which is the size of the necessary rod).

2. *Tapping Hole*
The diameter of the required hole for the tapping of an internal thread.

3. *Clearance Hole*
The diameter of the hole which allows the screw to pass through with easy clearance.

B.A.	Diameter	Tapping	Clearance
0	$\frac{15}{64}$	$\frac{13}{64}$	$\frac{1}{4}$
2	$\frac{3}{16}$	$\frac{5}{32}$	$\frac{13}{64}$
4	$\frac{9}{64}$	$\frac{1}{8}$	$\frac{5}{32}$
6	$\frac{7}{64}$	$\frac{3}{32}$	$\frac{1}{8}$

CHAPTER IX

HEATING METHODS

Applications of Heat—Sources of Heat—Gas Heating—The Blowpipe—The Air-blast—Blowpipe Control—Types of Blowpipe Flame—The Mouth Blowpipe—Other Sources of Heat—Petrol Vaporizer—Vapour Lamps—Comparative Temperature.

SOME processes of the craft are so dependent upon heat that its efficient application becomes a matter of extreme importance.

Before a piece of metal can be worked easily it is frequently necessary to anneal or soften it by raising its temperature and then cooling it. During its working, any shaping process will rapidly harden it either by compression or tension, and annealing is again necessary to restore the softness essential for further shaping.

The jointing processes demand the fusion of either soft-solder or silver-solder, each requiring a very precise application of heat. The former is regarded as a low-temperature process, the latter as a high-temperature one, the silver-solder fusing only at red heat.

In the making or adapting of special tools, red heat is necessary in the preliminary shaping operations or forging of the tool-steel, also in the annealing of the forged tool so that it may be easily filed to its final shape and again, to harden the finished tool-point. A range of lower temperatures is required for the last process of tempering, or reducing the extreme brittleness and imparting toughness.

Each of the foregoing instances of heat-treatment requires its own definite method to ensure the success of the particular operation. There are, however, two general rules applicable to any heating process. The first demands the even and gradual application of heat. The raising of temperature causes a movement in the internal structure which produces expansion to a varying degree in most metals. It also causes a molecular rearrangement, relieving the strains which a piece of metal may have acquired during a shaping operation.

Heating should therefore be even, so that the expansion may be constant throughout the metal, and gradual, to avoid the production of internal stresses due to violent rearrangement which may, in some instances, be the cause of fracture.

44

The sudden heating of a shaped piece of metal which is free to move, may merely cause twisting, but in a piece of work built up by the jointing of a number of parts (some of which will not be free to expand) may result in very serious distortion, the correction of which will be extremely difficult.

For the same reasons, local heating should be avoided and, wherever possible, the whole of a piece of work should be evenly and gradually heated.

The second general rule is concerned with excess of heat. The minimum temperature necessary in any operation requiring heat is the correct one. Nothing is gained by overheating and it is the frequent cause of serious damage.

Silver, copper, gilding-metal and brass are annealed when these metals become dull red hot. Continued heating will not make them appreciably softer. Overheating will produce a movement of metal on the surface which impairs its smoothness or else causes partial or complete fusion.

The overheating of a soft-soldered joint will be the cause of oxidation, which may prevent the fused soft-solder from flushing or flowing freely between the joint surfaces.

A silver-soldered joint is easily damaged by overheating. If easy-running silver-solder is used, its constitution may be changed due to the prolonged volatilization of the zinc, making the joint more brittle and leaving its surface rough and pitted.

Tool-steel is particularly susceptible to damage by overheating, which will cause a change in its character and properties due to the loss of its carbon content, if heated beyond a full red heat.

No heating operation should be performed in a strong light, as under this condition minimum temperatures are difficult to judge.

Sources of Heat

From the rude wood fire fanned by the breeze which was used by the earliest workers, to the modern applications of the electric arc, is a long and interesting chapter in the history of metalworking. Medieval craftsmen relied solely on the charcoal fire, and an amazing skill in its control is proved by examples of the most delicate filigree and in the intricate assembly and jointing of their work, which may be seen in museums and private collections.

The invention of coal-gas made the gas blowpipe, with its easily controlled air-blast and gas supply, available. This considerably simplified the difficult jointing operations.

The more modern heating flames, oxy-acetylene, oxy-coal-gas and oxy-hydrogen, also the electric arc, are not suited to the hand processes of hammered metalwork which require a comparatively slow application and even distribution of heat. Owing to their enormous heat, these oxygen-combined flames and the electric arc are invaluable in the jointing, cutting and melting operations of general metalwork where local heating or the application of intense heat is more desirable.

For the hand-forging of simple tools, a smith's open fire of coal or coke with an air-blast is still the most suitable.

Gas-heating Flames

The gas blowpipe with foot or mechanical blower, used with a soldering-hearth, is undoubtedly the most efficient heating medium for hammered metalwork. A domestic gas-ring may also be used for some forms of soft-soldered jointing and the annealing of small work. Many small silver-soldered joints may be made with the patented forms of bunsen burner which give a hot clean flame. The control of heat by these latter methods is so restricted in comparison with the flexibility of the blowpipe, that where a gas service exists, their installation would hardly seem justified unless they would be useful as auxiliary apparatus as, for instance, in a school workshop.

The Blowpipe

A similar range of work to that described in Chapter XXIX can be executed with a $\frac{3}{8}$ inch blowpipe, provided that the conservation of heat during the various operations is given attention.

A larger blowpipe is desirable and the $\frac{1}{2}$ and $\frac{3}{4}$ inch are more suitable, though the gas consumption of the latter is high. The size of the gas service pipe is important as, of course, a $\frac{3}{4}$ inch blowpipe cannot be operated from a $\frac{3}{8}$ inch service, as the gas pressure would be too low to produce the size of flame for which the blowpipe is designed. A large gas service can feed a small blowpipe, as it is then merely a matter of input control.

The Air-blast

A variable air-blast to a blowpipe is required to produce, in conjunction with the control of the supply of gas, the several definite types of flame necessary, the size and heating value of which vary between wide limits.

It is desirable that the air-blast should be constant at its source, the control being effected at the blowpipe.

A motor-driven blower is the most convenient, as the operator is then free to move round the soldering-hearth if necessary. The foot-bellows is the usual type in a small workshop, and should for preference be double-acting so that air-blast is obtained on both the upward and downward movements. When single-acting bellows are used, an air reservoir between the bellows and blowpipe is useful to smooth the pulsating air-blast and give a steady output.

BLOWPIPE CONTROL

Control of a blowpipe is generally effected by one of two methods. The first has independent control of gas and air supply in the form of taps on the blowpipe. The second is an automatic control in which the gas and air are regulated proportionately by one lever. The first arrangement is desirable as it permits of a much greater latitude of adjustment, and is capable of producing any of the required flames by a suitable setting of the taps.

The essentials of a gas blowpipe are two brass tubes, one for gas and the other for air-blast which terminate in a double concentric nozzle. Gas emerges from an outer sleeve, the end of which is contracted in order to give the flame a good shape. In the centre of the sleeve is a smaller nozzle similarly contracted so that its air-blast is directed forwards through the hollow centre of the ring of coal-gas flame.

It follows, therefore, that at the nozzle end of the flame the gases consist of an outer ring of cool flame and an inner cone of air which is rushing forward under pressure, carrying the gas flame with it.

In a short time they mix and burn fiercely, and to a metalworker this is the only useful part of the flame. Its exact location varies with the proportion of gas to air and also with the type of blowpipe flame, but is usually situated at about two-thirds of the flame-length from the nozzle end. In all blowpipe operations it is essential that its position is known and made the best use of. If the part of the flame nearer the nozzle impinges on the work, it will be only the cool ring of coal-gas flame with a centre of warm air, and if the extremity of the flame is used, it will certainly be hotter, though much of its heat will have been lost in combustion at the area where the gases mix. Also, the flame should be applied at right-angles to the work whenever possible.

A fierce roaring flame with ample air-blast is called a hard flame, and a quieter flame with restricted air-blast, a soft flame.

TYPES OF BLOWPIPE FLAME

The important flames are briefly described, and it is necessary that they may be produced at will during working (Plate 12).

Pencil Flame

A small thin, tapering flame with about equal small gas and air openings. It is usually obtained with a small blowpipe and is used mainly for flushing soft-soldered joints and for very small work where comparatively little heat is required.

Small Hard

A hot fierce flame of small size with equal medium gas and air openings for flushing small silver-soldered joints.

Small Soft

A flame which is produced with a small gas and a still smaller air opening. It is necessary as a preliminary evaporating flame in all silver-soldered work and for the annealing and pre-heating of small work.

Large Hard

This flame represents the full heating capacity of the blowpipe, and is obtained by full gas and large air openings. It is used where the maximum heat is required in the flushing of large joints and in the heating of big masses of metal.

Large Soft

The general annealing and pre-heating flame for use in all cases where even and gradual heating is required. It is produced by medium gas and small air openings.

Large Brush

A large brush flame is the full capacity of the blowpipe for soft flames, with the largest gas and medium air openings and is used for the pre-heating of larger work.

THE MOUTH BLOWPIPE

For jewellery, filigree and all very small work where an ordinary blowpipe flame would be too large and unwieldy, a mouth blowpipe is used with a flame from a bunsen burner or spirit-lamp. Practice is required in order to produce an even flame of constant intensity. Control is obtained by the strength of the air-blast and also by the distance of the end of the mouth blowpipe from the flame (Plate 12).

OTHER SOURCES OF HEAT

The foregoing heating methods presuppose a gas service. Where this does not exist other means must be adopted which are not so convenient. Work may be annealed in an open coke fire or on a clean red coal fire. Turning will be necessary and also care in handling with tongs. Silver-soldering is also possible by this method, but the process will demand a much higher degree of skill than with gas.

The finest medieval work in metal was executed with the aid of a char-coal fire or furnace, using hand-bellows as air-blast.

Probably the best modern substitute for coal-gas is found in the petrol vaporizer (Plate 49), an arrangement which depends for its action on the volatility of petrol. Its outstanding merit is the fact that the ordinary blow-pipe with its wide range of control is used. Two arrangements are suggested in Chapter XXVIII, the chief requirements being a petrol tank having a large number of wicks suspended in the spirit, a gas outlet and a safe method of warming the petrol, the whole to comply with any existing fire regulations.

A substitute for a gas blowpipe is the vapour lamp, either a blowlamp or the larger brazing-lamp.

Paraffin is vaporized by the heat of the nozzle of the lamp and the gas is forced through a tiny jet, burning fiercely with a blue roaring flame. The feed of oil to the vaporizer is maintained by air-pressure from a small pump in the container.

The disadvantage of the vapour-lamp is the lack of control of the flame, and other methods of heat-regulation must be adopted which usually consist of varying the distance of the flame from the work, packing with fire-brick or screening part of the work with asbestos sheet.

In the case of very small work the absence of gas is no handicap, as a mouth blowpipe is effectively used with a small spirit-lamp.

COMPARATIVE TEMPERATURE

A table of comparative temperature is given, showing metallic fusing-points, ranges of temperature of the heating processes, also incandescent and oxidation colours relative to temperature (page 196).

4

CHAPTER X

BENDING

General Methods—Thin Wires—Thick Wires and Mouldings—Edge Mouldings—Thick Strip, Rod and Bar—Cylinders and Cones in Sheet Metal—Decorative Bent Wire.

BENDING is probably the simplest of the shaping processes and is concerned with the production of curves in one dimension, e.g. a ring of moulding, a handle or the cylindrical body of a canister.

The first requirement is an estimation of the total length of metal required to form the curve. This is, in the case of rings and parts of circles, a matter of simple calculation.

For irregular shapes such as handles, it is usually sufficient if a piece of thin wire is bent to the required curve on the drawing of the work, cut to the correct length, then straightened out and measured.

Metal should be annealed before bending and it sometimes becomes necessary to re-anneal before the finished shape is reached, especially if the material is thick or in cases where a good deal of alteration has taken place.

Hand-pressure over a former or stake should be employed whenever possible. A mallet will be necessary when dealing with thick metal or if the radius of the curve required is small. (Hammers should on no account be used for any ordinary bending operation.)

THIN WIRES are bent in flat and round-nosed pliers, pressure with the thumb being applied as near to the pliers as possible (Plate 13, Fig. 1).

THICK WIRES AND MOULDINGS are bent over suitably shaped stakes and formers, held either vertically or horizontally in the vice. Circles are bent in three stages on a former, the diameter of which should be slightly less than that required. The material will spring to a larger diameter when released from the former (Plate 13, Fig. 3).

NARROW EDGE MOULDINGS which are bent in the single length for the edges of polygonal plates and trays (Example No. 9, Plate 55), should have each corner bend made and carefully checked on a full-sized drawing before proceeding to the next one. Care is also required in the flatting and general finishing adjustments so that the sides of the figure remain true.

THICK STRIP, ROD AND BAR may be bent over a length of round bar held horizontally in the vice. The application of pressure or point of impact of the mallet should be in advance of the point of contact of the work on the bar (Plate 13, Fig. 2).

CYLINDERS AND CONES IN SHEET METAL are shaped conveniently in three stages on a cylindrical stake, funnel stake or bick-iron, depending upon the shape and size of the work. The bending is commenced by hand pressure, the form being finally trued with a mallet (Plate 13, Fig. 4, *a*, *b* and *c*). A bick-iron or funnel stake should not be used for the bending of any cylindrical shape, e.g. a ring of $\frac{1}{4} \times \frac{1}{8}$ inch metal. These stakes are conical and will produce a distorted bend in other than conical forms.

DECORATIVE BENT WIRE

An example is given of the building up of a decorative handle by wire bending and silver-soldering (Plate 14).

Two 5 inch lengths of $\frac{1}{8}$ inch round annealed wire are bent to loops by hand pressure and malleting round a short length of $\frac{3}{8}$ inch round steel rod held vertically in a vice (Figs. 1, 2 and 3).

The loops are then bent upward to 45 degrees (by malleting on the bench corner or on a piece of wood) and threaded together and pulled up tightly (Figs. 4, 5 and 6).

A third piece of wire is inserted between the loops (Fig. 7), and the whole squeezed in the vice between two pieces of soft wood (Fig. 8).

The waste is sawn off, $\frac{1}{4}$ inch from the loops, the ends tied with binding-wire and bevelled by two 45 degree file cuts forming square pointed ends (Fig. 9). Square notches are filed in the ends of a 9 inch length of $\frac{1}{4} \times \frac{1}{8}$ inch metal, which is bent to a circle. The wire handle is inserted, tied with binding-wire and silver-soldered with hard-running silver-solder (Fig. 10).

The circle is then cut and the ends flatted, filed to a slow taper and finally oval (Fig. 11). The completed handle is now bent to shape, the waste removed, the ends rounded and the whole cleaned off (Fig. 12).

It is silver-soldered to the work by easy-running silver-solder.

CHAPTER XI

FOLDING

Folding Method—Narrow Strip in Thin Metal—Narrow Strip in Thick Metal—Right-angle Folds in Sheet Metal—Wide Folds—Long Folds—Rectangular Box Sides—Folding Heavy-gauge Metal.

FOLDING is a bending process which produces flat faces and angular corners as distinct from curved surfaces. Many of its requirements are similar to those of bending—estimation of length, annealed metal, hand pressure and finishing with a mallet.

The light use of a convex hammer for finally sharpening folded corners is permissible, provided that it is realized that with the use of the hammer a small amount of stretching of the metal must inevitably occur.

THIN METAL is folded over a square bar in the vice with one of its corners uppermost (Plate 15, Fig. 1). When the shape is attained the corners will be rounded.

The square bar is then held in the vice with a flat face uppermost and the faces of the work are malleted on to it, carefully working up the sharp corners from adjacent faces.

The final process may consist of finishing the corners by using a convex hammer very lightly on the flat faces, working right up to the corners, leaving them sharp (as in Plate 28, Fig. 2).

Wide metal may also be folded in this way, though if a flat bar is used, difficulty may be experienced in keeping the faces flat in their length. The tendency is for them to become concave and this may be minimized by the use of a square bar which has been shaped very slightly convex in its length.

THICK METAL requires different treatment, as it is impossible by the foregoing method to fold a sharp corner in this material. The inside surfaces will be in compression and will bulge sideways at the internal angle. The outside surfaces will be in tension and will contract sideways at the external angle. There will also be an appreciable rounding of the corner on the outside, and if an attempt is made to sharpen this by flatting the faces, the metal will be seriously thinned.

The most satisfactory method consists of cutting grooves across the metal at the position of the corners with square or triangular files, depending on the required angle of the corner. The strip is then folded by hand pressure and the corners silver-soldered on the inside (Plate 15, Fig. 2).

It follows that the less metal left at the base of the groove the sharper will be the corner, so that just sufficient should be left to hold the strip together during the silver-soldering operation.

RIGHT-ANGLE FOLDS IN SHEET METAL may be made in folding-bars. The flat sheet is carefully inserted in the folding-bars so that the folding-line is just visible.

The bars are inserted in the vice, the fold being made first by hand pressure (Plate 15, Fig. 3, *a*). Then the corner is sharpened by malleting each face and finishing with a light convex planishing hammer (Plate 15, Fig. 3, *b*). Care should be taken to ensure that thinning does not take place due to over-hammering and that the surfaces are not damaged by sliding through the bars.

WORK WHICH IS TOO WIDE TO ENTER A VICE must be folded over the square edge of a metal block and must be malleted on adjacent faces alternately until the corner is sharp and the faces flat.

LONG FOLDS for which ordinary folding-bars cannot be used may be worked between two pieces of hardwood or square iron or steel bars, which are held in a vice at one end and in a G-cramp at the other. The work is gripped in the bars between the vice and cramp and folded over.

Difficulty may be experienced due to the tendency of the bars to bend hollow (away from each other at the centre) producing a folded corner of varying rounding, which is also concave in its length.

RECTANGULAR BOX SIDES can be folded on a block of hardwood held in the vice. Each side is, in turn, folded down by hand pressure applied as near to the corner as possible (Plate 15, Fig. 4, *a*). The corners are then sharpened with a mallet and the sides flatted (Plate 15, Fig. 4, *b*).

Another method is to fold an opposite pair of sides in folding-bars and to use the block for the remaining pair.

The inside edges of the ends of the sides should be bevelled with a file before folding, to make a correct mitre when folded. They are then silver-soldered.

HEAVY-GAUGE SHEET-METAL is folded by nicking or grooving the internal angle before folding, to define the corner and to make the folding easier. This is done with a chisel (ground at 90 degrees) and a light hammer, the work being supported on a smooth metal block during the process.

Extreme care is necessary to avoid stretching and distortion. When the folding is completed, the groove at the internal angle will be closed if it has been correctly worked and must be silver-soldered to strengthen it.

CHAPTER XII

HOLLOWING

Description of Process—Small Forms—Large Forms—Very Small Forms—Elliptical Forms.

HOLLOWING is a simple method of shaping sheet metal into shallow circular or elliptical forms curved in two dimensions, by hammering or malleting a disc of metal hollow, using a depression in a block of wood or sand-pad as a support. In hollowed work the shaping is executed on the inside of the form.

It is a process involving stretching by tension and, as such, will cause thinning of the metal, so that there is a limit to the depth of hollowed work which is reached when the depth exceeds one-third of the diameter.

It is, therefore, a process of shaping which must be restricted to low, shallow forms.

SMALL FORMS under six inches in diameter are hollowed in a gouged depression in a hardwood block with a hollowing hammer. The depression should be shallow and truly spherical and must not be regarded as a mould into which the metal is hammered in order to make a shape similar to the depression. It is merely a support for the work, varying shapes being produced by the different angles at which the work is held on the block or is struck by the hammer (Plate 16, Fig. 1, *a*, *b*, *c* and *d*).

An annealed flat disc is held firmly in the left hand with its front edge resting on the front edge of the depression in the hollowing-block, the disc being inclined at an angle of about 30 degrees to the horizontal.

It is then struck steadily by ' dead ' blows (without spring or rebound) at a point $\frac{1}{2}$ inch from the front edge, with a hollowing hammer. The disc is rotated slowly so that each hammer blow just overlaps the preceding one, no two blows falling in the same place on the metal.

After the first circle has been completed it will be noticed that the disc is now slightly twisted. This must be corrected by hand pressure on the disc over the corner of the bench (Plate 32, Fig. 1).

Succeeding circular courses of hammer blows are repeated in the same manner until the centre of the form, or limit of the desired hollowing, is reached.

The work is now annealed, pickled and scoured and the process repeated until the required depth is obtained.

The important rule to observe is that the point of impact of the hammer on the work is in front of (or in advance of), the point of contact of the work on the block, as by this means the metal is stretched down quite freely and quickly into the depression in the block.

If the point of impact and point of contact are coincident, i.e. if the metal is struck where it is solid on the block, a certain amount of shaping will take place, but under this condition the work expended is not being used to the best advantage. Moreover, the progress is much slower and the desired shape more difficult to obtain.

The centre of a bowl or similar shape will stretch more rapidly than the edge, due to the fact that the centre is surrounded and held rigidly by the hardened edge, so that progressively lighter blows should be struck as the centre is approached. A wavy edge should never be allowed to form. Slight irregularities in the edge should be corrected as they appear.

When finishing a shape, an inside templet should be used, which is a pattern of the shape required made in tinplate or card, and which is obtained from the elevation drawing (Plate 30, Fig. 1).

The final operation consists of truing up the work so that it correctly fits the templet and is at the same time truly circular in plan. Small irregularities in the surface are removed in readiness for the planishing process. Some profiles of hollowed forms are illustrated in Plate 17.

LARGE FORMS are hollowed on a sand-pad with doming mallet (Plate 16, Fig. 2). This is a rather more difficult process because the depression in the sand-pad is made by the action of the mallet forcing the metal into the pad, the sand of which is capable of movement in any direction.

The rigid depression in the wood block which assisted in maintaining a truly circular form is absent, therefore the work is more likely to twist and for the same reason the tensional stretching will be much slower.

VERY SMALL HOLLOWED FORMS are worked in a steel doming-block with round-nosed boxwood punches, commencing in the larger depressions and decreasing until the correct size is reached.

A lead block may replace the doming-block, and in this case a steel punch is used. A depression of the necessary size is first worked in the lead, in which the disc is hollowed (Plate 16, Fig. 3).

ELLIPTICAL FORMS are hollowed by similar methods. The tendency to twist is very much greater and must be corrected, especially in the early stages.

CHAPTER XIII

SINKING

Description of Process—Circular Sinking—Elliptical Sinking—Rectangular—Large Salvers.

SINKING is a hollowing process in which the centre of the form is sunk, leaving a margin of the original disc which becomes a flat rim in the final shape. The process is required in the construction of plates, trays and salvers.

An annealed disc is cut of the finished diameter with a small waste allowance, and an allowance is also made for a wired edge or waste margin.

The sinking-line is set out from the centre with spring-dividers or wing-compasses, if a circle, and by means of a metal templet if of any other shape (except, of course, rectangular and polygonal).

A hardwood block is used, on the end grain of which an arc of the outside circle is marked. Two round nails are driven in on this line and are used as a fence or stop.

CIRCULAR SINKING

The circle of metal is held by the left hand on the block in the vice, so that the edge of the metal is pressed against the stops. In this position the sinking-line will be exactly over the corner of the block if the stops have been inserted correctly.

The disc is then lightly struck by dead blows with an oval sinking hammer just inside the sinking-line, holding the disc horizontal against the force of the hammer blows and rotating it slowly until a hammered circle has been struck. This will produce a very shallow sinking of about $\frac{1}{8}$ inch in depth with a rounded upper corner (Plate 18, Fig. 1).

The next step is to sharpen this corner by malleting the rim on the block, which has been reversed in the vice, finishing with a light convex planishing hammer (Plate 18, Fig. 2).

If the elevation of the work is examined it will be found that the rim is perhaps slightly wavy and also that the sinking is buckled or twisted.

58

This condition must now be corrected and the work inverted on a polished flatting-block and the edge of the rim flatted with a mallet.

This will not correct the twist in the sinking, and it is necessary to use a piece of wood held on the rim, up against the sinking, for this purpose. It is struck fairly heavy blows with a bench hammer, slowly moving the wood round the rim until the inside of the rim is quite flat (Plate 18, Fig. 3). This operation will pull the corner of the sinking into contact with the block.

The work should now be reversed on the flatting-block and the base flatted with a small mallet (Plate 18, Fig. 4).

The foregoing processes represent a cycle of operations which must be repeated until the sinking is of the correct depth, annealing, pickling and scouring between each cycle. If the intermediate flatting and truing-up is omitted, the work will develop serious buckles which are extremely difficult to remove.

During the actual sinking, the hammer blows should strike the work as near to the corner as possible, sliding down the sinking with a pulling action towards the worker. This materially assists in keeping the corner a good shape.

The final operation consists of carefully truing up and flatting the work, then annealing, pickling and scouring in readiness for planishing.

A steel stake, having a square corner very slightly rounded off, may replace the wood sinking-block. Its action is more precise, as the working edge does not become depressed as in the case of the wood edge. Unless, however, it is handled skilfully, the damage to the under side of the metal will be considerable.

ELLIPTICAL SINKING is worked in the same way as circular sinking, but, as in hollowing, the tendency to twist is very much greater.

RECTANGULAR AND POLYGONAL SINKING is executed by the same method, except that a round hollowing hammer must replace the sinking hammer when the corners of the rectangle or polygon are being worked. Further, a much larger waste allowance must be made, as the long sides of a rectangle will be considerably drawn in.

LARGE SALVERS are frequently too heavy to support with one hand comfortably, and should be slung. A pulley is screwed in the ceiling of the workshop a few feet in front of the vice. A cord carrying at one end a suitable weight, is passed over the pulley and attached to a hand vice which grips the far edge of the salver. The weight of the work is thus balanced and it is only necessary to guide it on the block and to move the hand-vice round the edge of the salver as the work proceeds.

CHAPTER XIV

STRETCHING

Definition and Application—External Stretching—Internal Stretching—Summary.

STRETCHING is an extremely important process in shaping, in which sheet metal is compressed between the surfaces of a hammer and anvil or stake and is spread out and thinned as a result.

Stretching is present in any form of hollowing, but it is then stretching by tension. When the term stretching is used to indicate a process, stretching by compression is implied.

Its most useful and frequent application in hammered metalwork is when it is used to increase, for purposes of shaping, the original diameter of circular forms.

It may be executed by two methods, depending upon whether the hammering process is worked on the outside or inside of the shape that is being stretched.

EXTERNAL STRETCHING

If, as an experiment, the end of a thin stick of soft-solder is held on the face of a flat stake and struck with a flat hammer a number of blows, it will be found that the surface area at the end of the stick has been increased.

There has, of course, been no actual gain as the increase in area has been at the expense of the metal thickness.

Also it will be observed that the increase in area has been fairly constant so far as the direction of the spreading is concerned. It has been expanded in width as well as in length an equal amount. The metal has been compressed and squeezed forwards and sideways and at the same time made thinner.

It has, therefore, been stretched but by compression instead of by tension as in the case of a piece of sheet metal which has been hollowed in the depression of a hollowing-block or sand-pad.

If a similar experiment is repeated on another stick of soft-solder, this time using a convex instead of a flat hammer, it will be noticed that the

61

spreading is produced more quickly. If the same number and weight of blows have been given, the surface area at the end of the second solder stick will be greater than that of the first.

This is because the metal offers less resistance to the smaller area of the convex hammer at the instant of impact and allows it to penetrate further into the metal. As it does so, the convex face forces the metal out and away from its centre in all directions.

A hammer used for the process of external stretching should, therefore, have a slightly rounded or convex face.

If a similar process is applied to a cylindrical or conical form, the same result will be obtained. As another experiment, a funnel stake or bick-iron is held in a vice and a seamed truncated cone of sheet metal is slipped over the projecting end of the stake. The cone is slowly rotated on the stake and struck near one end with a convex hammer until a complete hammered circle has been given, the facets of which just overlap each other.

Each hammer blow will stretch (or spread outwards) the small area of metal upon which it falls, and their combined effect will be to produce an increase of surface area at the end of the cone at the expense of the metal thickness.

The increase in one direction will add length to the cone and the increase in the other direction will force it to assume a larger diameter. (The diameter, however, will increase more than the height, due to the shape of the stake and its action upon the metal, for a reason which will be more apparent when internal stretching is considered.)

If the cone is annealed and the hammering commenced farther back, (Plate 19, Fig. 1, a), and continued to the end (Plate 19, Fig. 1, b), so that several overlapping hammered circles are given, the diameter will be progressively increased from the beginning of the hammering to the end of the cone, thus illustrating the principle of the process of external stretching. The point of impact and point of contact must be co-incident.

A ring of thick strip may be stretched conical from a cylindrical form by being hammered near one edge whilst being rotated on a bick-iron (Plate 19, Fig. 4).

INTERNAL STRETCHING

This operation is a more rapid application of the stretching process, but it can only be used when the shape and size of the work permit of its being hammered on the inside, when its lower surface is supported on a suitably curved stake (Plate 19, Fig. 3).

If, as a further experiment, another stick of soft-solder is held on a flat stake and is struck a number of blows at the end, this time with a collet hammer, it will be found to have been considerably stretched.

In this instance, the amount of stretching in each direction is by no means equal. The increase will be much greater in the length than in the breadth, due to the shape of the collet hammer face, which is curved in one direction only and which has expanded the metal forwards and backwards at each blow, but considerably less sideways.

If conditions are reversed and a stick of soft-solder is held at right-angles on a cylindrical stake and is struck with a flat hammer at the point where the metal rests on the stake, the result will be precisely similar and unequal stretching will take place, this time due to the shape of the stake, which acts in the same way as a collet hammer.

These two experiments illustrate an important principle in metal shaping generally. It is the basis of the process of 'drawing down' and 'fullering' in forged work, and it finds another application in the internal stretching of cylindrical and conical forms in sheet metal.

In the process of internal stretching, cylindrical and conical forms are held on the top of the curved surface of a funnel or cylindrically shaped stake, with their axes at right-angles (Plate 19, Fig. 3).

Small work, a bowl-mounting, for instance, is struck internally with a small collet hammer and slowly rotated, keeping it at a constant angle on the stake. (A collet hammer having a curvature of large radius must be used for work of larger diameter so that the hammer face is as good a fit as possible on the curved surface of the work being internally stretched.) The operation will produce a spiral of hammer blows, commencing where the stretching is intended to start and finishing at the edge or end of the form. By this means its diameter is stretched and the metal expanded over the stake, the curvature of which it is made to assume.

The same process may be executed on a short length of $1\frac{1}{2} \times \frac{3}{4}$ inch tool-steel or mild-steel bar, one edge of which has been shaped to the required profile (Plate 19, Fig. 2, *a* and *b*, and Plate 52).

The process of internal stretching is not difficult after some practice, but its action is rather complex.

Each hammer blow, if it is struck where the work is solid on the stake, i.e. if the point of impact and point of contact are co-incident, has two distinct effects which combine to produce the stretching.

Firstly, the stretching action in one direction only by the collet hammer on the upper surface of the metal, expanding the metal before and behind it, thus increasing the diameter of the work.

The second stretching action, again in one direction, is by the stake on the lower surface of the metal. The stake, being of a similar shape, is acting to a less degree as a second collet hammer, and since the curvature of the stake is at right-angles to that of the hammer, it follows that the direction of the stretching due to the stake will be at right-angles to that due to the hammer.

Therefore, not only will the diameter of the work be rapidly increased by the first action, but the metal will also be stretched in the other direction by the second action.

If the work is now hammered so that the point of impact is in advance of the point of contact, then a third action will operate. The metal will be driven farther round and thus expanded to the curvature of the stake by tensional stretching before it is actually compressed between the hammer and stake at the instant of impact.

The internal stretching method is so rapid that it should be used wherever possible, but the deciding factors will be the size and shape of the particular work in hand and also the amount of thinning which can be tolerated.

Tall narrow forms must be stretched externally, whilst low cylindrical and conical shapes usually permit of the internal method being used.

SUMMARY

1. Stretching by tension, as in hollowing.
2. Stretching by compression.
    (*a*) External stretching with convex stretching hammer. Point of impact and point of contact co-incident.
    (*b*) Internal stretching with collet hammer. Point of impact in advance of point of contact.

CHAPTER XV

CONTRACTING

Description of Process—Convex Contraction—Concave Contraction—Contracting a Turned-down Rim—Convex Contraction by Planishing.

CONTRACTING is a shaping process by which the original diameter of a circular form is diminished by compression. In a sense it is the inverse process of stretching in so far as it produces an opposite result.

A piece of sheet metal of any shape may be stretched by hammering, but a contraction process is only applicable to sheet metal already in a circular form, the diameter of which may be reduced by some application of the process.

The several methods by which this result is obtained bear little relation to each other.

CONVEX CONTRACTION

The profile of cylindrical, conical and spherical forms may be contracted simply by hammering in spiral or concentric courses over a stake shaped to the desired curve (Plate 20, Fig. 1, *a*, *b* and *c*, and Plate 52).

It is necessary that the work be supported by the stake for a considerable distance behind the point at which the contraction commences, as otherwise the resistance or back-pressure offered by a stake which is only in contact with the work at one point, or on a small area, will cause serious bulging and distortion behind the contraction.

A flat or convex hammer is used, depending upon the shape of the work, and its point of impact must be in advance of the point of contact of the stake, so forcing the metal, as the work is slowly rotated, round the curvature of the stake, the result being a progressive decrease in its diameter.

CONCAVE CONTRACTION

Cylindrical and conical forms may be contracted to a concave profile by hammering into a concave stake with a collet hammer, commencing at the edge and working to the centre or point of maximum concavity (Plate 20, Fig. 3, and Plate 52).

5

With this operation a small amount of stretching by tension at the edges usually takes place. As the diameter at the centre decreases so the diameter at the edges will increase slightly by tensional stretching at the points of contact on the stake.

It is often necessary to combine this application of the process of contraction with that of stretching intentionally.   In the shaping of a seamed bowl-mounting, for instance, it is desirable to work the contracted concave profile, first by a contraction process, then to finish the shape by internally stretching the metal near the edges.

It should also be realized that concave contraction can entirely replace the process of internal stretching in the shaping of work of this nature.

CONTRACTING A TURNED-DOWN RIM OR FILLET

A horizontal rim is contracted to a vertical form on a canister stake or on the end of a round bar (Plate 20).   The work is held on the stake with the metal to be contracted projecting over the stake and is struck by light, glancing mallet blows, as the work is slowly rotated until the rim is turned down (Fig. 2, *a* and *b*).   If very much metal is to be turned, i.e. if the finished vertical height exceeds $\frac{1}{8}$ inch, the operation must be performed in two or more stages, contracting a little more metal each time.   If a wide rim is attempted in one operation, serious distortion may result.   The final operation consists of sharpening the slightly rounded corner, first with a convex hammer on the top of the corner (Fig. 2, *c*), and secondly with a flat hammer on the vertical side (Fig. 2, *d*).

CONVEX CONTRACTION BY PLANISHING

A vertical edge of a tray, bowl or similar form may be contracted and planished in the one operation provided that only a slight contraction is required.   The point of impact must be in advance of the point of contact and not co-incident, as in ordinary planishing.   A flat hammer is used (Plate 20, Fig. 4).

CHAPTER XVI

PRODUCTION OF SEAMED FORMS

Description—Circular Seamed Forms—Elliptical Seamed Forms—Polygonal Seamed Forms.

THE easiest method of shaping tall forms is by bending or folding sheet metal and then silver-soldering the free edges together, to produce a three-dimensional form (Plate 37, Fig. 3). The method is a useful one in elementary work, to which it should be restricted. It usually involves the fitting and jointing of a base either by soft- or silver-soldering (Plate 38, Fig. 6), so that the completed form will contain two joints, a vertical butt seam and a horizontal base joint.

This jointing method is undesirable in any advanced work, which should always be shaped by raising the one piece of metal from the flat sheet, thus producing the required form and its base without a joint (Plate 24, Fig. 1).

Raising from the flat is admittedly not an elementary process, and as elementary work often requires the production of tall forms, the method of shaping by seaming is, therefore, included as a process.

CIRCULAR SEAMED FORMS

These forms are invariably commenced from cylinders or truncated cones, and the procedure, details of which are included in relevant chapters, is to estimate the size of the commencing form from the working drawing. A pattern, usually in cartridge paper, is developed and the metal cut to it and bent to the circular form. The ends are then carefully fitted to form a butt joint with square edges and silver-soldered with a good-quality easy-running silver-solder and the completed seam cleaned off on both surfaces.

It is seldom that a simple cylinder or truncated cone is required in that form. More often they are the commencing forms for shapes having convex or concave profiles, or a combination of both. This further shaping is executed by processes of stretching or contracting, either separately or in combination.

If a butt seam is correctly made with the right grade of silver-solder, the work will withstand a very considerable alteration from its original form by these processes of hammered shaping. The edges of the prepared joint must fit evenly so that the silver-solder in the finished joint is of constant cross-sectional area throughout the length of the seam. The silver-solder must be of similar malleability to the metal which it joins so that it will stretch at the same rate as the metal. Hard-running silver-solder is comparatively brittle and will readily fracture. Frequent annealing during any shaping operation is necessary, as the silver-solder forming the joint hardens by hammering at a quicker rate than does the surrounding metal.

Typical circular seamed forms are illustrated in Plate 21. The upper ones are examples of those required for tankards, vases and beakers and the lower ones include those used in the making of napkin-rings and seamed bowl-mountings.

Elliptical Seamed Forms

These forms are either bent and seamed as circular forms and then malleted elliptic before any further shaping takes place, or they may be bent elliptic and seamed in that form.

Polygonal Seamed Forms

Prisms and truncated pyramids are occasionally required. They may be produced either by folding to their required form and then seaming, or they can sometimes be bent and seamed in a circular form, the flat faces being produced later by a process of panelling (Plate 25). In this latter instance, the seam should be arranged to occur at the centre of a flat face.

CHAPTER XVII

RAISING

Description, Application and Methods—Raising with Wedge Mallet—Raising with Hammer—Faults—Raising Large Work—Raising Straight-sided Forms—Raising Curved Profiles—Panelling—Control of Metal Thickness during Raising—Caulking—Comparison of Raising by Mallet and Hammer—Action of the Process of Raising.

RAISING is the process for the production of all shaped forms which are contracted from a flat disc of sheet metal.

In hollowing, the metal is worked on the inside of the form commencing at the edge of the upper face of the work and continuing inwards, towards the centre, the metal being stretched tensionally down into the depression of a hollowing-block. The consequent thinning of the metal limits the depth to which a form may be hollowed.

Raised forms are worked on the outside, commencing at the base on the under side of the work and continuing to the edge, by a contracting operation on a stake which raises the rim and so produces the height of the form.

Because raising is a contraction process and does not, therefore, entail tensional stretching, the metal is not thinned during the operation and the form may be raised as tall as the metal will allow.

Raising may entirely replace hollowing for the production of even very shallow forms and in high-class work hollowing is seldom employed.

In more advanced work, the process of raising is used to produce the forms which in elementary work were obtained by bending and seaming either cylinders or cones. A low bowl-mounting, for example, is raised to an appropriate profile from a disc of metal. The flat centre is then removed, leaving the required form without a joint. Further shaping from this stage, if necessary, is executed by processes of stretching or contraction.

Raising was the shaping process of the medieval craftsman and it should be regarded as the basic hand-shaping process of modern hammered work.

Spinning is its mechanical equivalent. In raising, the shaping of the metal is produced by slow rotation under percussion and in spinning by high-speed rotation under pressure.

The process of raising may be executed by two methods.

The first consists of contracting the metal on a stake having a double curvature—either a ball, dome or mushroom stake, using a boxwood wedge mallet which has a working face shaped like a large collet hammer.

The second method makes use of a steel raising stake, the essential feature of which is an arm, straight in its length and curved across its breadth with a radius of about $1\frac{1}{2}$ inches. The metal is contracted on this stake with a raising hammer having a rectangular face such as a collet hammer, but almost flat, with its sharp corners and edges removed. Its working face may be $1\frac{1}{4}$ inches wide and $\frac{3}{16}$ to $\frac{3}{8}$ inch thick.

Raising with Wedge Mallet (Plate 22)

An annealed disc of metal has a circle struck from its centre corresponding approximately to the size of the base of the form. Concentric circles at $\frac{1}{2}$ inch intervals are also lightly struck to act as guide circles.

The disc is held on a ball, dome or mushroom stake with the left hand, at an angle of about 30 degrees to the horizontal, with the top of the base circle over the stake. It is then struck even blows with a wedge mallet about $\frac{1}{2}$ inch above its point of contact with the stake, i.e. on the first guide-circle. The disc is held very rigidly against the force of the mallet blows with the left hand and slowly rotated so that successive blows do not fall in the same place on the metal.

When a complete hammered circle has been struck it will be observed that an indentation has been formed by the metal having been contracted over the rounded profile of the stake. Succeeding hammered circles, commencing where the last finished, will force the indentation higher up the disc towards the edge. When the edge is reached the diameter will have been contracted and a shallow raised form produced (Plate 22, Figs. 1 and 2).

The work should now be trued up, annealed, pickled and scoured, and if a taller form is required, the foregoing operations are repeated several times until the height is obtained (Plate 22, Figs. 3 and 4).

As the work proceeds, it may be found convenient to invert it, if a ball stake is being used, and strike downwards with the mallet (Plate 22, Figs. 5 and 6).

The shape of the required profile will, in shallow raised work, decide the type of stake to be used. Shallow forms may be raised on a dome stake and deeper forms on a ball stake. The flatter curvature of a mushroom stake is convenient for work having a relatively straight profile.

RAISING WITH HAMMER (Plate 23)

This operation is commenced with an annealed disc on which is struck the base circle and lightly applied guide-circles having a $\frac{3}{8}$ inch interval. It is held at about 20 to 30 degrees to the horizontal, with the top of the base-circle over the tip of the raising stake. A lightly hammered circle with the raising hammer is commenced just above the base-circle. Owing to the angle at which the disc is held, the front edge of the hammer strikes the metal first, and in so doing depresses it on to the horizontal surface of the raising stake (Plate 23, Fig. 1). The disc is slowly rotated until this hammered circle is completed, further circles then being struck between the concentric guide-circles until the top edge is reached, thus finishing the first course of raising.

The work must be held very firmly at a constant angle against the force of the hammer, and the indentation which is formed at the commencement of the operation carried steadily up to the edge. If this indentation is lost, then the process becomes simply stretching by compression between hammer and stake and the diameter of the disc will not be decreased. If the depth of the indentation is appreciably increased during the progress of the work, the metal between it and the edge of the form will be too high to depress on to the face of the stake and will soon become uncontrollable.

Further, the raising hammer must fall squarely on to the work, depressing the metal about $\frac{3}{8}$ inch nearer to the rim (i.e. the metal immediately over the indentation) firmly and decisively on to the stake by the front edge of the hammer. When this is done correctly it will be accompanied by a solid-sounding metallic click. If not, the sound will be hollow, indicating that the metal has not been brought into contact with the stake.

During most of the operation, a point about 1 inch from the tip of the stake should be used. To enable this to happen, the work must be moved back on the stake as the edge is approached. This is to prevent the tip of the stake from continually pressing against the inside of the base corner and so causing stretching by tension and consequent thinning.

Also, the drawing back of the work as the edge is approached gives a better balance, the weight of the job behind the stake tip assisting in holding it against the force of the hammer blows.

When the first course has been completed, a low raised form with a sloping side should have been produced (Plate 23, Fig. 2). It is annealed, pickled and scoured. The next course is commenced, holding the work at a very slightly increased angle and a new indentation formed which is again carried up to the edge (Plate 23, Figs. 3 and 4). A succession of these operations will finally give a form with a vertical side.

Should a form with a contracted mouth be required, the hammered courses are continued, commencing higher up the profile (Plate 23, Figs. 5 and 6).

FAULTS

A wavy top edge should be corrected as it forms by removing the peaks, striking them at their bases and working them out to the edge. If they are allowed to remain, they tend to develop into folds. Should a fold be struck over with the hammer, the only cure is to remove a complete strip of metal from the whole of the edge. If an attempt is made to remedy a hammered fold, the affected metal will probably crack during a subsequent hammered course of raising.

Accidental misuse of a raising hammer will produce pitted blemishes, causing serious local thinning of the metal. Unfortunately, these defects cannot be removed by planishing, an operation which compresses the metal into contact with the surface of the stake. The thinning of the metal then appears as isolated pits or else as shallow grooves which follow the original circles of the defective hammering.

The fault is usually due to the incorrect angle of impact of the hammer, the face of which must always be horizontal when it strikes the metal. A lack of restraint in the weight of the hammer blows will produce a similar defect, which will be accentuated if the hammer itself is too heavy and also if its corners are insufficiently rounded.

RAISING LARGE WORK

When raising large work, the raising stake is mounted in a low stand. The operator is seated at a stool of convenient height, pressure being applied to hold the work steady against the force of the hammer blows by the knees.

RAISING STRAIGHT-SIDED FORMS

Theoretically, these forms should be raised with a straight profile throughout the whole process, commencing each hammered course at the base corner and finishing it at the rim. To maintain the straight profile it is necessary that the contraction of the form be greater near the rim than at the base, so that each course is commenced with a very small indentation at the base corner and is progressively increased as the rim is approached. The base-angle decrement which is the result of this operation is illustrated in Plate 27 (D).

To ensure that the final indentation near the rim is not too large to depress effectively, the commencing indentation must be exceedingly small. The repeated hammering of these very small indented courses near the base, which do not appreciably contract the form, tends to thin the metal in that area.

In practice, therefore, it is usual to commence each hammered course with a normal indentation which remains constant until the rim is reached. When this happens, a concave-sided form will result, due to the increased contraction near the base. To produce a straight-sided form from this stage, successive courses are commenced, not at the base, but at points progressively higher up the profile. This method is quicker and it does not entail the over-hammering and consequent thinning of the metal near the base of the form.

RAISING CURVED PROFILES

Owing to the fact that a raising stake is flat in its length, it follows that some tall curved profiles cannot be raised directly by the hammer method.

Concave profiles are quite straightforward as they are raised on the stake, using a hammer, by increasing the contraction at the base of the form, alternatively by allowing the indentation of successive courses to diminish as it ascends the form, thus progressively reducing the contraction at the top.

Convex profiles must be worked in two stages by the hammer method. The profile is worked as a series of flats by moving commencing levels of the raising to points higher up the profile.

At the completion of the work, the flats may be merged into the finished convex profile by malleting on a suitably shaped stake, or they may be stretched up from the inside by means of a snarling-iron. The work is pressed down and slowly rotated on the ball of the snarling-iron. The shank is struck with a bench hammer at a point along its length which will cause a rebound upwards of the ball end of the tool (Plate 24, Fig. 2).

Panelling

Raised forms which are polygonal in plan, e.g. an octagonal vase or beaker, are first raised as circular forms. The flat faces are then produced by panelling. They are malleted on to a hardwood block which is of similar shape and size to one of the required faces (Plate 25). The base corners require slight stretching from the inside, which is executed with a snarling-iron, the end of which is forged and finished to a suitable shape.

Control of Metal Thickness during Raising

When using a raising hammer, beginners frequently thin the metal. If the blows are so heavy that more energy is expended than is necessary to strike the metal into contact with the stake, the metal will be compressed between the hammer face and stake after contact with the stake has been made. This will produce stretching by compression and will operate in opposition to the contracting action of the raising process. This is not so important, as it is slight by comparison; what does matter is the fact that the metal is being needlessly thinned. The hammer blows given should be of such a weight that their energy is expended almost at the instant the necessary three-point contact is made between the hammer, metal and stake.

A raising hammer having a slightly convex face will thin the metal, due to a collet-hammer action.

Caulking

If the edge of a raised form is required to finish thicker than its original gauge, it may be thickened progressively during the raising operation by a process of caulking. Before annealing, at the completion of each hammered course, the edge of the metal (i.e. the metal thickness) is struck a course of dead blows in line with the sloping side of the form with a convex or collet hammer, the work being pressed on to a sand-pad by the left hand (Plate 25). This operation at the end of each course of raising, when the edge of the metal is sufficiently hard to withstand the impact without buckling too much, will compress the metal at the edge and thicken it very slightly. The edge is then trued and the work annealed. The cumulative effect of the process is appreciably to thicken the edge of the metal as the work proceeds. It is extremely useful in strengthening the edges of forms of large diameter.

Comparison of Raising by Mallet and Hammer

There is probably little to choose between the two methods as regards ease of working. Any raising operation is difficult until a reasonable amount of practice has been obtained.

The hammer method is by far the quicker, though accidental damage due to careless use of the tool is likely to prove more disastrous than in the case of the mallet. Further, the tooled surface from the hammer requires more planishing than does the smoother surface left by the mallet. In hammer raising, the aim should be to produce a good surface by the light use of the hammer in the final courses.

In the choice of method it is wise to be guided by the shape of the work and the suitability of available equipment. Wide and shallow forms are frequently raised by the mallet and a hammer is invariably used for tall or narrow forms.

Examples of raised forms are illustrated in Plate 26.

Summarized Action of the Process of Raising

At the commencement of the raising operation, the initial contracting of the metal at the base circle forms an identation which is forced up the form from the base to the top edge by ascending concentric circles of mallet or hammer blows.

As the indentation moves gradually towards the top, the diameter of the form behind it is contracted. The metal that is made surplus by the decrease in diameter (and which has to be accommodated) has no alternative but to be forced downwards and forwards under the mallet or hammer face at the instant of impact, the cumulative effect of which is to add height to the form as its diameter is contracted.

If a molecule of metal situated immediately in front of the indentation is considered theoretically during the raising operation, it will be realized that the impact of the hammer will give it a diagonal movement. It will be forced downwards to the stake surface and will, at the same time, move forwards under the hammer face so that it finally occupies a position in advance of its original one. The downward movement will reduce the diameter of the form at that point and the forward movement will increase its height (Plate 27, C and R).

CHAPTER XVIII

PLANISHING

The Object of Planishing—Planishing Hammers—Preparation for Planishing—Planishing Method—Radial Planishing—Spiral and Concentric Planishing—Grouped Planishing—Planishing on Pitch—Planishing on Lead—Examples of Planishing.

AFTER a piece of metal has been shaped by malleting or hammering, its surface will usually be slightly irregular and uneven. If it has been stretched by tension, as in a hollowing process, its surface may also be rough. When it is examined by means of a powerful magnifying glass, the surface of the metal will appear to possess a granular texture. There may also be irregularities due to uneven shaping, caused by the inexperienced use of a tool.

A finishing process called planishing is, therefore, necessary to remove these defects. Planishing consists of the even and regular hammering of a metal surface on a well-fitting stake with a light, polished hammer. Its purpose is neither to continue the shaping of the work nor to alter its form, but to true it and close the grain of the metal, removing any unevenness and irregularity from its surface. Neither is its object the covering of a surface with hammer marks to create or accentuate a hand-made appearance, an artifice sometimes in favour with manufacturers of mass-produced metalwork in a vain effort to impart the character of hand work to something rolled out of a machine.

Planishing aims at the production of smooth and true surfaces by the use of a hammer. Every time a piece of metal is struck by a hammer where it is solidly supported on a stake, a mark, indentation or facet will be made on each side of the metal, as a result of the compression. It is therefore apparent that a well-planished surface is one on which the hammering or faceting is unobtrusive.

PLANISHING HAMMERS

As an experiment, three pieces of annealed copper are, in turn, held on a flat stake and hammered. The first with a hollowing hammer, the second with a stretching hammer and the last with an ordinary flat bench hammer.

The surface of the first will be deeply pitted by tiny hammer marks which have penetrated far into the metal.

The second will show a decided improvement. The pitting will not be so deep, also individual marks or indentations will be larger.

The surface of the last one is further improved, with an absence of coarse indented marking. It will, however, be marred by scars caused by the corner of the hammer face.

The correct hammer, therefore, for the planishing of flat surfaces will be one whose face is imperceptibly rounded or convex and whose corner is very thoroughly rounded off. It is a hammer which is by no means easy to use in an unpractised hand, but which is, nevertheless, the correct one.

To continue the experiment, a small hollowed bowl or similar form is held on a well-fitting ball stake. Three patches on its surface are hammered with the same hammers as previously. In the case of numbers one and two, the former unsatisfactory results are now intensified—due to the smaller area on the curved surface covered by the hammers at each blow. In the last case, however, the effect is this time correct, because the corner of the hammer face which produced defects on the flat surface cannot cause trouble, owing to the curvature of the work. Therefore, for convex surfaces, a flat hammer is the correct one and it is also desirable to round off the sharp corner so that less damage may be caused in the event of an accident.

For flat surfaces—a convex planishing hammer.

For convex surfaces—a flat planishing hammer.

The weight of the heads of both the convex and flat planishing hammers may be from 4 to 8 oz.

The stake must be so chosen that its curvature is as near to that of the work as possible. The radius of its curvature should be slightly less than that of the work to be planished. It must never be greater. If this happens, the work will be distorted during the process. Neither should it exactly equal it. Planishing is a compression process and, as such, will stretch the work very slightly. If a stake exactly fits a job at first, consequent planishing may stretch the work out of contact with the stake, which will again cause distortion.

PREPARATION FOR PLANISHING

Before work is planished it must be inspected for scratches and blemishes. These must be carefully removed by the methods suggested in Chapter VI.

Planishing should not be relied upon to cover up defects in a surface. It will only make them more difficult to remove later. The work must also be trued up as much as possible in the final shaping operation.

It should be annealed, pickled, scoured with pumice powder and water, rinsed and dried.

The hammer and stake must be cleaned for use and polished bright and means should be provided for keeping them in a polished condition during working. (Dirty metal causes a fouled hammer face.)

Planishing Method

During planishing, the hammer must be held at a point of easy balance, pivoting at the wrist and not at the elbow, which should be pressed tightly to the side. The stake and work must be at a comfortable height in the vice and the work is held in contact with the stake firmly and decisively. The fall of the hammer should be square on to the work and the point of impact and the point of contact must be co-incident. Extremely light and 'dead' hammering is always a necessity in any planishing operation, the hammer being pressed on to the work without appreciable spring or rebound.

The metal is compressed lightly between the hammer and stake and receives an impression of the hammer on its upper surface and of the stake on its lower surface. The hammer blows should fall evenly over the same place on the stake, the work being rotated or moved so that no two blows are given to the same place on the work and that no gaps are left.

Each facet should slightly overlap the preceding one, and lines or courses of facets must overlap preceding ones. If the facets or courses are too close to each other, ridges will be produced and also the metal is needlessly stretched.

Planishing may take one of the three following forms :

Radial Planishing

In this arrangement the facets approximately follow radial lines from the centre to the edge. It is a convenient method of planishing small flat circular surfaces, as it assists in keeping the work flat. It is also used for finally truing up large curved work, planished by other methods.

Spiral and Concentric Planishing

This is the usual way in which to planish small circular forms, commencing at the centre and finishing at the edge as a continuous spiral of facets, or in concentric circles. The centre of a form will stretch quickly and be forced upwards away from the stake, a tendency which demands very light working at or near the centre. The extreme edge must be planished lightly to avoid stretching and consequent distortion of the form.

Concentric pencil circles should be struck on circular forms about half an inch apart or less, to act as guide-lines.

GROUPED PLANISHING

Large work or a shape for which a properly fitting stake is not available is planished by another method. The facets are arranged in small groupings, the size of a sixpence, each of which merges into its neighbour until the work is completed. For this and, of course, other methods of planishing, it is often necessary to use two or more stakes for the planishing of one job. Care is needed to ensure that ridges are not formed where the work of one stake merges into that of another. If this occurs, it often becomes necessary to re-planish the work radially.

PLANISHING ON PITCH

Occasionally a form is required to be planished for which a well-fitting stake cannot be found. When planishing contracted raised work, its mouth or opening may be too small to allow the correct stake to enter it. The vessel may be filled with a hot composition of two parts Swedish pitch and one part plaster-of-paris which have been previously mixed in a pail on a gas-ring. When the composition is cool and has set hard, the work is rested on either a sand-pad or a circle made by coiling and tying a leather strap or thin rope, and is planished with suitably shaped hammers. The pitch is heated and run out when the operation is finished and the inside cleaned off with paraffin. On no account must the heating be done with a blowpipe or loose flame. Local heating may cause a burst, due to the expansion of imprisoned gases. The work should be heated slowly in an oven.

PLANISHING ON LEAD

An alternative method for the planishing of small complex forms is to rouge the inside of the vessel and then very thoroughly to dry it. Molten lead which has been melted in an iron pot is then slowly poured in and allowed to set and cool. Minor shaping operations and planishing are very easily executed on such a solid base, which acts as a well-fitting stake. When finished, the work should be inverted and the lead melted out by gradual heating with a blowpipe flame at its lower extremity. (Great care is required in the use of molten lead.)

EXAMPLES OF PLANISHING

FLAT PLANISHING.—The flat rim of a small tray or plate is planished on a flat stake by grouping, with a convex hammer (Plate 28, Fig. 1). It must be planished very lightly to prevent stretching, which will produce a wavy rim. The base may be planished radially with a convex hammer on a flat stake or polished flatting-block. Bases of large trays and salvers are planished by grouping, and 'set,' i.e. brought into contact with the flatting-block and made to set rigidly without buckles. A large-faced hammer is used, of the minimum possible convexity. As the size of this type of work increases, so does its difficulty, which becomes one of controlling the stretching of the large flat circular base. The setting of a large salver is a highly skilled job where a very few hammer blows will either make successful or ruin an attempt. The centre forming the base may sometimes be planished before the sinking is commenced and set as a final operation.

The flat faces of hexagonal or octagonal work are planished by grouping on the face of a square bar with a convex hammer (Plate 28, Fig. 2). Stretching will produce concavity of the side.

CYLINDRICAL forms are planished spirally or concentrically on a side stake or cylindrical stake with a convex hammer (Plate 28, Fig. 3). Stretching will produce concavity. (The most suitable stake is a specially made cylindrical type (Plate 52), being turned slightly convex in its length, so that it makes contact with the work at one point only.)

CONICAL forms are planished spirally or concentrically on a funnel stake or bick-iron with a convex hammer (Plate 28, Fig. 4). Stretching will again produce concavity.

BASES are planished radially on canister stakes with a convex hammer (Plate 28, Fig. 5). Stretching produces a doming of the base on the inside of the form.

SPHERICAL and similar forms are planished spirally or concentrically on ball or dome stakes with flat hammers (Plate 28, Fig. 6). Stretching near the centre and edge will seriously distort the shape.

SMALL SINKINGS are planished on their external surface, spirally on a radius stake or small cow-tongue stake with a flat hammer. The radii of the stake must be slightly smaller than that of the sinking in each direction (Plate 29, Fig. 1).

LARGE SINKINGS are planished internally with a large sinking hammer in concentric courses, the sinking being supported on its convex or under side on a flat stake, at the necessary angle (Plate 29, Fig. 3).

CONVEX SIDES of small raised or hollowed work are planished externally with a flat hammer on suitable cow-tongue, ball or dome stakes or on detachable planishing heads held in a ' horse ' (Plate 29, Fig. 2).

CONCAVE PLANISHING is executed with a collet hammer if its curvature is suitable (Plate 29, Fig. 4).

INTERNAL PLANISHING.—A horizontal bowl rim is planished on its upper or internal surface with a convex planishing hammer on a cylindrical stake (Plate 29, Fig. 5).

COMPLEX or tall contracted forms are planished on a filling of lead or pitch with suitable hammers, as previously described (Plate 29, Fig. 6).

6

CHAPTER XIX

TESTING METHODS

Need for Testing—Straight Edges—Corners and Angles—Flat Circles—Irregular Curves—Flat Surfaces—Cylinders—Cones and Pyramids—Hollowed Work—Sinkings—Raised Work—Upper Edges—Bases.

WHEN a finished example of hammered metalwork is examined, it should be found to be reasonably accurate, if its form is considered as a whole. Its base should be even and flat, allowing it to stand rigidly. If its form is circular, rotation in the hand should not disclose any large irregularities. Lids and moving parts should work smoothly and fit correctly. The work should be symmetrical, and, in a word—true.

To ensure that a job passes successfully through all its shaping processes to this desired end, it is necessary to apply simple tests every time its shape is altered. If errors are allowed to pass at one stage, they will be carried through to the next and confirmed. Correction is then made much more difficult, if not impossible.

Especially is this true of built-up work jointed from several parts. Inaccuracies in one part often make a modification necessary in another, and if this is continued through the whole work the cumulative error will produce a form which is far removed from the dimensions of the working drawing. Errors may, of course, cancel each other out in the building up of an advanced piece of work, but unfortunately they are more often additive.

The necessary testing methods which should be used as the work proceeds are usually so simple that they are but the work of a few seconds.

STRAIGHT EDGES are tested by straight-edges, normally in the form of a 12 inch steel rule. They may also be checked by their contact on a surface-plate.

CORNERS AND ANGLES.—Right-angles are tested with a try-square. A 4 inch engineer's pattern is suitable for small work and a 12 inch woodworker's pattern for larger. Angles other than right-angles are tested with a sliding bevel which is set by means of a protractor.

FLAT CIRCLES may, of course, be checked for circularity with a pair of wing-compasses or spring-dividers. In cases where the centring of the compasses presents difficulties, e.g. a circle of wire or moulding, they must be placed on a similar pencil circle drawn on paper.

IRREGULAR CURVES should always be both set out and tested by a templet cut in tinplate.

FLAT SURFACES may be tested by means of a metal straight-edge or by their contact with the face of a surface-plate.

CIRCULAR RIMS can be tested for truth by comparative measurements made with a scriber across two or more diameters (Plate 30, Fig. 2).

CYLINDERS are examined for circularity and parallelism with outside calipers (Plate 30, Fig. 3), and for squareness of end by rotation against a try-square on a surface-plate (Plate 30, Fig. 5).

CONES AND PYRAMIDS may have their slope and symmetry tested by setting a bevel to the supplement of their base-angle in elevation (180 degrees—base-angle). The work is rotated against the bevel which is used on a surface-plate (as in Plate 30, Fig. 5).

HOLLOWED WORK.—Its depth and profile are tested by the use of an internal templet made from the elevation drawing, allowance being made for the metal thickness (Plate 30, Fig. 1).

SINKINGS are tested by means of a templet as in hollowed work.

RAISED WORK may be examined for truth by being rotated against a templet of its profile on a surface-plate. Another method makes use of two pencil circles. A pencil resting on a piece of wood on a surface-plate is used to describe a circle round the work near its top (Plate 30, Fig. 4, *a*). A second circle is struck with pencil compasses from the original centre of the disc, which is now the centre of the base, the compasses being set to the first circle (Plate 30, Fig. 4, *b*). If the circles are co-incident when the second one is completed, the work is true. If not, the difference between the circles exposes the error.

UPPER EDGES may be tested for parallelism with their bases by being rotated to the needle of a scribing-block on a surface-plate (Plate 30, Fig. 6). They may also be checked for flatness by inverting the work on the surface-plate.

BASES may be checked for flatness by placing them on a surface-plate. If the base is gently rubbed in short strokes on the surface-plate the shiny patches made by the friction indicate the high places.

CHAPTER XX

METHODS OF TRUING AND ADJUSTING

Flatting Sheet Metal—Straightening Wire—Flatting Moulding—Straightening Small Tube—Flatting and Truing a Circle of Wire—Truing Cylindrical and Conical Forms—Truing Hollowed Work—Levelling a Vertical Edge—Levelling a Horizontal Edge—Truing a Large Sinking—Truing Raised Work.

THE operations of truing and adjusting as applied to hammered metal-work do not consist of a final tidying-up process in an effort to right all the wrongs and correct the small inaccuracies which have accumulated since the commencement of a job. It would then be too late. Many of these would now be permanent reminders that the truing-up and adjusting should have commenced earlier. From the cutting of the material to the final polishing, the truing and adjusting operations should be considered a part of the work as important and necessary as the major shaping processes. If this method of working is adopted, large inaccuracies will not make their appearance, as the work will not be far from truth at any time. As in the case of the continual care of the surfaces, the truing operations become, through time, almost automatic. In the preceding chapter the methods of testing and revealing the inaccuracies were discussed. Suggestions are now given for their correction.

FLATTING SHEET METAL

Sheet metal is placed on a flatting-block and its high places are struck down into contact with the surface of the block with a mallet. The metal is reversed and the operation repeated until every part of its surface is in contact with the block (Plate 7, Fig. 4).

STRAIGHTENING WIRE

Thin wires are straightened by a slight tensional stretching. One end is held in a vice and the other in pliers or draw-tongs and the wire roughly straightened by hand. It is then pulled steadily until the pliers are felt to 'give' slightly, indicating that the wire is commencing to stretch. It will then be straight (Plate 31, Fig. 1).

FLATTING MOULDING

Thick wire and mouldings cannot be easily straightened by stretching. Flat mouldings must be straightened both edge-wise and flat-wise on a flatting-block with a mallet (Plate 31, Fig. 2). It is usually easier to flat the edge first.

STRAIGHTENING SMALL TUBE

Small tubes and short lengths of annealed wire are straightened by being rolled on the flatting-block under some hard flat surface (Plate 31, Fig. 3). If a mallet is used on tube it will cause distortion, which may, however, be corrected by pulling the tube through a suitable drawplate hole.

FLATTING AND TRUING A CIRCLE OF WIRE

The truing of a wire circle is a very important operation, the need for which constantly arises. It should be realized that two distinct operations are necessary—(a) flatting and (b) truing its circularity. These are to some extent interdependent. Flatting will often alter the circularity adjustment and vice versa, so that the two operations should be worked alternately until the circle is true both ways. The flatting is done on a flatting-block with a mallet (Plate 31, Fig. 4). Then a position is found on the slope of a funnel stake, bick-iron, or tapered mandrel which fits the curvature of the circle. The wire circle is slowly rotated, keeping it in the same position on the stake and is lightly struck with a mallet (Plate 31, Fig. 5). The truing takes place when peaks or high parts are struck down on to the curved face of the stake as they pass under the mallet. This operation may have affected the flatting, which must now be repeated.

TRUING CYLINDRICAL AND CONICAL FORMS

The usual requirement is the truing of the circularity. It may be corrected on a cylindrical stake, funnel stake or bick-iron, and the operation consists, as previously, of malleting the peaks in the curved surface down on to the stake (Plate 31, Fig. 6).

Occasionally, as a result of incorrect planishing which has caused a stretching at the ends, these forms become concave in their length. They are then trued by re-planishing at, and near the centre, firstly as a fairly narrow band and finally as a wider one, until the work is flat in its length (Plate 31, Fig. 7). It should be realized that the job will finish very slightly larger as a result, due to the extra planishing.

A better alternative consists in the contraction of the stretched ends of the cylinder back to the original diameter on a cylindrical-type stake which is slightly convex in its length (Plate 52).

TRUING HOLLOWED WORK

In the early stages of hollowing, the work frequently develops a twist. If inverted on a surface-plate it may appear concave and when rotated 90 degrees it will appear convex. It should be placed over the corner of a bench and corrected by hand pressure (Plate 32, Fig. 1).

LEVELLING A VERTICAL EDGE

If the depth of low hollowed work is uneven, accompanied by distortion of the circle, when viewed in plan, it should be pressed down tightly on to a flatting-block and the top edge struck lightly with a hammer at its highest part. This will true the uneven depth, at the same time restoring the circularity to the top edge (Plate 32, Fig. 2). (This method is only applicable to a low hollowing having a flat base.)

LEVELLING A HORIZONTAL EDGE

An uneven or wavy horizontal bowl edge should be rotated to a scribing-block needle and its inaccurate parts indicated with a pencil. The work is trued on a suitable stake with a mallet or hammer. Parts that are high (i.e. those above the scribing-block needle) are depressed and the low parts raised until the whole edge is reasonably true (Plate 32, Fig. 3). It is then inverted on a flatting-block and the edge finally flatted with a mallet.

TRUING A LARGE SINKING

The general truing of sunk work should be done during the actual process and consists of working exactly to the sinking-line in plan and to the correct depth in elevation and also flatting the base and rim. During the planishing of a salver distortion may occur, producing 'loose' or 'tight' metal at the centre which is the cause of buckling. After the planishing of the base is completed and the work trued up, the centre of the salver may feel springy and move suddenly either upwards or downwards like the base of an oil-can when pressure is applied. The centre then is loose, i.e. it is in compression. The remedy is lightly to hammer the base near to the sinking, all round the salver, stretching it slightly and expanding it outwards, drawing the compressed centre with it.

Occasionally a sunk base finishes so loose that no correction with a planishing hammer is effective. The sinking in that case should be struck a circular course of blows, downwards and inwards at 45 degrees with the sinking hammer, in order to draw the sinking away from the centre, which has the effect of tightening the loose metal (Plate 32, Fig. 4).

The opposite case is the tight centre, in which the metal at the centre is in tension. The sinking and rim will not lie flat, due to a pulling action by the tight centre. The treatment is lightly to hammer the centre of the base, stretching it slightly and relieving the strain on the sinking and rim.

TRUING RAISED WORK

Truing an unevenly raised form may be confusing if the requirements are not understood. The conditions are illustrated in the case of a very simple raised form. When viewed in elevation the base-angles are unequal and the top edge is out of parallel with the base (Plate 32, Fig. 5, a). When viewed in plan, the top and base circles are eccentric. The remedy at first sight would appear to consist of cutting the top edge to a new horizontal height-line, but it is apparent that if this were done the base angles would still remain unequal and the circles eccentric. The real defect is that part of the form has not been raised as much as the remainder and the cure is obviously to continue the raising on the part of the form that is low. It must be done progressively from the base to the top edge, not as the usual complete hammered circle but in part circles which commence at the base and increase in length until the top edge is reached. This operation is, of course, only applied to the part of the form which is insufficiently raised and must be repeated until the whole form is true (Plate 32, Fig. 5, b). It is, fortunately, not a common fault, but nevertheless one that should be watched for, as it becomes increasingly difficult to correct as the raising proceeds.

If, in raising, the hammering is executed as an ascending spiral instead of in concentric circles, a tall form will tend to pull over out-of-true and therefore not vertical in elevation. This effect will cancel out if alternate spiral courses are rotated in opposite directions.

CHAPTER XXI

FILING AND FITTING

The Aim in Filing—Filing Method—Types of File and Their Uses—Edge Filing—Mouldings, Tubes and Wires—Protection of Surfaces—Fitting Methods—Reduction of Wires and Tubes—Fitting Edges—Fitting Circles of Wire and Narrow Strip—Fitting Circles of Moulding and Corded Wires—Fitting Moulding to a Spherical or Double Curved Surface—Handle Fitting.

THE use of the file in hammered metalwork is not sufficiently frequent to give the process of filing the same fundamental importance that it has in general metalwork. Apart from shaping and fitting during the progress of the work, the use of the file is restricted to cleaning off in preparation for the polishing process.

The relatively small part it plays in comparison with other tools is, however, of the utmost importance. It is responsible for the final shape of the joints, corners, angles and edges on which it is used and upon its precision depends to a large extent the good appearance of the finished work. For this reason it is important that its correct use is mastered so that it is not employed in the cleaning-off operations to the detriment of the finish of the work.

A file should not be regarded as something to rub metal with to make it smooth. Water-of-Ayr stone will do that very effectively. It is a cutting-tool to be used to true up surfaces and edges, its smoothing effect being a secondary consideration.

If a file is used to true up a small flat surface, the work should be finished truly flat. It must not be high at its centre, gradually falling away towards the edges. The corners must be left sharp, and if they are required to be slightly rounded off, such rounding must be done by the file as a definite second operation.

When a flat edge is trued with a file, it must be finished flat and not be filed in the centre only where the operation is easiest. The ends must also receive attention and the whole edge should be made straight and at right-angles to its adjacent surface.

When a curved surface is trued with a file, the finished result must be free from 'rounded-over flats' which deflect the light falling upon them.

89

A high light on an accurately filed curving surface should appear to be evenly continuous, conforming to the shape of the work. (This may often be used as a valuable test in the truing of curved work.)

It is, of course, easy to suggest a list of requirements. In this, as in every craft worthy of the name, precision can only be obtained by practice and concentration.

FILING METHOD

The method of holding a file depends upon whether it is to be used for heavy or light filing. For work where heavy downward pressure is necessary, the palm of the left hand is placed over the end of the file with the fingers extended naturally.

For light work, a thumb-and-finger grip by the left hand is more suitable. The handle is grasped easily and firmly by the right hand for either method. The file is held so that the blade is maintained horizontally during the full length of each stroke, pressure being applied on the forward stroke only, which should utilize the full length of the blade.

TYPES OF FILES AND THEIR USES

Ten-inch flat and half-round second-cut files are suitable for heavy work. For lighter work and the finer shaping operations, 6 inch flat, half-round, round, square and triangular files are used. Waste is removed with the second-cut grade and the finishing is executed with a smooth or dead-smooth grade. The shape of the file should be chosen so that it fits the work as nearly as possible.

Knife-edge and warding files are useful for many fitting and cleaning-off operations, and an assorted set of Swiss files is almost indispensable. A 10 inch woodworker's half-round rasp is frequently useful in the shaping of wood blocks and formers and for the shaping of mallet faces.

Every file should be securely fitted with a suitable-sized handle and on no account should a file be used without a handle. When files are used on copper they readily become clogged by filings, which should be cleaned off by frequent use of the file-card or wire brush. Pinning, as this is termed, may be minimized by rubbing the file with chalk before and during use. A file should never be used on a wet surface.

EDGE FILING

The edge of a long piece of sheet metal must be supported during a filing operation either in folding-bars or between pieces of wood (Plate 33,

Fig. 1). When filing a seam for fitting, it is convenient to arrange it in the vice so that the edges can be brought into contact frequently for testing (Plate 33, Fig. 2).

Draw filing is a method of finishing an edge or narrow surface by holding a smooth file sideways and horizontally, allowing it to cut on both forward and backward strokes.

A safe-edged file is useful in the filing of an internal angle when it is desired to remove metal from only one edge or surface.

MOULDINGS, TUBES AND WIRES

A hardened steel joint-tool must be used in which to hold mouldings, tubes and wires, the slightly projecting ends of which are squared with a file for the purpose of fitting a butt joint (Plate 33, Fig. 3).

PROTECTION OF SURFACES

Work held in a vice for filing must be protected from the serrated vice jaws by means of vice clams, which are angle-pieces of soft copper or lead the width of the jaws (Plate 33, Fig. 2). Polished or planished surfaces must be gripped in a vice between cardboard or thick paper, in addition to the metal clams, to prevent scratching. Vulcanized fibre clams are also useful for work of this nature.

There is always the danger of the file slipping on to a hammered surface when cleaning off wired and folded edges. A piece of adhesive tape wrapped round the work under the edge will prevent damage. The work should be supported on a piece of wood in the vice to allow of easy rotation (Plate 33, Fig. 5).

When filing over or near to a flat surface, it is often desirable to protect it from accidental damage from the tip of the file, by gumming a piece of paper over it. It is washed off when the operation is finished.

FITTING METHODS

The more important general methods are included under this heading.

Reduction of Wires and Tubes

Wires may be reduced in gauge for purposes of fitting, e.g. hinge-pins, by being drawn through progressively smaller holes in a draw-plate. The end of the wire is pointed and inserted in a suitable hole, with the draw-plate in the vice. The projecting end is gripped in draw-tongs or heavy pliers and pulled steadily through.   The draw-plate holes are lubricated with tallow and frequent annealing of the wire is necessary.   Small tubes may be reduced by the same method (Plate 33, Fig. 4).

Fitting Edges

Vertical edges of circular forms are ground flat on a carborundum or emery rubbing-stone used dry (Plate 33, Fig. 6).   Sandstone and water may be used, though its cutting action is comparatively slow.   Finishing of the rough edge is done on a sheet of fine emery-cloth on a flatting-block.

Fitting Circles of Wire and Narrow Strip

Circles of rectangular wire and narrow strip should be bent and silver-soldered so that they are just too small for a desired fitting.   They are then stretched to the correct diameter by planishing on a suitable cylindrical stake and a very fine adjustment may be obtained if the hammering is restrained.   If the strip has any appreciable width, it is necessary to ensure that it is very carefully planished so that distortion due to uneven stretching is avoided.   This will occur at the edges unless they are hammered very lightly.

Fitting Circles of Moulding and Corded Wires

In the fitting of circles of applied moulding and corded wires to circular forms, the same method is adopted.   The circle is bent and jointed with hard-running silver-solder and is of a diameter which is very slightly less than that required, so that in fitting the circle it has to be strained or pushed into position, possibly by pressure with a piece of wood. Any appreciable stretching which may be required must be executed with a mallet on a cylindrical stake or flatting-block, depending upon whether the moulding is bent edge-wise or in the flat.   Restraint must be exercised in stretching corded wires, as the stretching is very rapid even with a mallet, due to the fact that the upper wire is pressed into the lower one by the impact of the mallet blow, producing elongation of the pair of wires.

Fitting Moulding to a Spherical or Double-curved Surface

It is necessary to pre-determine a development curve as explained in Chapter V (Plate 6, Fig. 9).   The required length of moulding is cal-culated and a small waste allowance made.   It is annealed and one end squared in a joint-tool and then bent in the flat to fit the development curve. The squared end is pinned to the bowl in its correct position, and the circle of moulding gradually pressed in to the side of the bowl and secured with split-pins at inch intervals. When this takes place, the inner face of the moulding will automatically assume the angle of the side of the bowl, due to its having been previously bent in the flat to the development curve, allowing it to fit accurately at its upper and lower edges. The position of the applied wire is finally adjusted, the waste overlap marked and cut off and the ends fitted and pinned to the bowl. The moulding is removed from the bowl and its butt joint made with hard-running silver-solder. It is cleaned off and re-applied to the bowl and jointed to it with easy-running silver-solder, or soft-solder as required.

Handle Fitting

Vulcanized fibre, ebonite, wood and other non-metallic handles are fitted in handle sockets by a process of draw-pinning. The handle is cut to shape and cleaned off and the shoulder-lines marked with a scriber from the handle sockets (Plate 34, Fig. 1). The tenons are cut with a brass-back saw and carefully fitted and finished (Plate 34, Figs. 2 and 3). A $\frac{1}{16}$ inch pin-hole is drilled in the sockets and its location marked on the tenons with the handle in position, as a tiny circle, made with a finely pointed scriber (Plate 34, Fig. 4). The pin-hole in the tenons is drilled, not on the centre of this scribed circle, but at the point on its circumference nearest the tenon shoulder (Plate 34, Fig. 5). When the handle is replaced, the holes do not accurately register. Well-fitting pins are prepared from $\frac{1}{16}$ inch wire, having one end tapered. These are now inserted and lightly tapped through, causing the holes to be drawn into alignment, thus cramping the shoulders tightly up to the ends of the handle sockets (Plate 34, Fig. 6). The pins are withdrawn and their projecting ends neatly rounded off. They are re-inserted when the handle is finally fixed.

CHAPTER XXII

SOFT-SOLDERING

Description of Process—Soft-solder—Flux—Types of Soft-soldered Joints—Soft-soldering Methods—Procedure—Double-process Soft-soldering—Tinned Joint—Loaded Joint—Single-process Soft-soldering—Pre-determined Application—Direct Application—Examples of Soft-soldered Joints—Cleaning off Soft-soldered Joints—Faults—Choice of Soft-soldering Method.

SOFT-SOLDERING is a metal-jointing process in which an alloy of tin and lead is fused on to the surfaces of the joint. For elementary work in hammered metalwork soft-soldering is an easy jointing method.

It is a comparatively low-temperature process, the solder fusing at a point which is considerably below the temperature at which copper, gilding-metal and brass are annealed. Work that is soft-soldered as a last operation is therefore left hard from planishing.

Whilst it is permissible for simple work in the base metals, mainly on account of its relative cheapness and ease of handling, soft-soldered joints are only of moderate strength and should not be used in the jointing of any advanced work.

The process should be regarded as a subsidiary method, silver-soldering being the basic jointing process of the craft.

Soft-soldering should never be used in the assembly of any work in silver, not because it is less efficient in this metal, but because silver in no matter how simple usage is always worthy of silver-soldering.

SOFT-SOLDER

Several grades of soft-solder are available, some being used for specialized work. A generally suitable grade is known as 'fine' soft-solder, and consists of 2 parts of tin and 1 of lead. Blowpipe or 'medium' soft-solder may also be used, which fuses at a slightly higher temperature and is an alloy of equal parts of tin and lead.

FLUX

When metal is heated in making a soldered joint, the oxygen of the air combines with its surface, producing an oxide which prevents the flow of the molten solder. The presence of dirt and impurities on the surfaces of the joint will have a similar effect. An agent known as a flux is required to keep the metal surfaces clean during the jointing operation. The most serviceable flux for the class of soft-soldering under consideration is zinc-chloride.

The cleaning action commences as soon as the liquid is applied to the joint. When heated it gives off hydrochloric acid vapour, the cleaning action of which continues until all the flux has been evaporated.

It may be prepared by placing concentrated hydrochloric acid in an earthenware pan in the open air and adding zinc to it. When the ebullition has ceased and the addition of more zinc has no effect, it is left to stand for some hours and then strained through fine muslin. The resultant solution should be used without the addition of water.

TYPES OF SOFT-SOLDERED JOINT

There are only two types of soft-soldered joint usually applicable to hammered metalwork:—

(*a*) Surface-to-surface joints.
(*b*) Edge-to-surface joints.

SOFT-SOLDERING METHODS

The commonly accepted method of soft-soldering, such as would be used in the repair of a kettle by the direct use of a soldering-bit or the method of making joints directly with the soldering-bit as employed by a craftsman in tinplate, may be almost entirely discounted so far as hammered metalwork is concerned. The method which is effective for tinplate (sheet mild-steel coated with tin, which is a constituent of soft-solder), has certain disadvantages when applied to hammered metalwork. It is not sufficiently precise. The flow of the molten metal is difficult to confine and control generally, so that other methods must be used.

The various operations of soft-soldering in hammered metalwork differ mainly in the methods by which the soft-solder is applied to the joint. They may be conveniently classified as follows:—

1. DOUBLE-PROCESS SOFT-SOLDERING

(*a*) *Tinned Joint*

One surface of joint previously tinned (Plate 35, Figs. 1 and 2).

(b) Loaded Joint

One surface of joint previously loaded or liberally tinned (Plate 35, Figs. 3 and 4).

2. SINGLE-PROCESS SOFT-SOLDERING

(a) Pre-determined Application

Joint previously charged with cut pieces of soft-solder (Plate 36, Fig. 1).

(b) Direct Application

Joint fed directly from a soft-solder stick (Plate 36, Fig. 4).

PROCEDURE

The essentials of each method are described.

1. DOUBLE-PROCESS SOFT-SOLDERING

In this method of soft-soldering it is more convenient to apply the soft-solder in two distinct stages, the first of which consists of the application of soft-solder by means of a soldering-bit to one part of the joint. The second stage is the assembling of the fitted joint and the fusing of the soft-solder, already on one of them, with a blowpipe flame. The joint is ' flushed,' i.e. the molten soft-solder flows between the surfaces of both parts of the joint, uniting them by a thin film of soft-solder which firmly and solidly adheres to the surfaces when set.   (This method is often known as ' sweating.')   There are two applications :—

(a) Tinned Joint

This joint is used when two surfaces are being united, for example, a circle of flat moulding to sheet metal. The relatively large surface-area allows of a strong joint being made, using very little soft-solder, therefore one surface is ' tinned ' or evenly and thinly covered with soft-solder, using a soldering-bit for this preliminary application (Plate 35, Fig. 1).

The Soldering-bit

Before a soldering-bit can be used, its working faces must also be tinned so that the applied soft-solder can cover its surface easily. A new soldering-bit must be heated to just under red heat, cleaned with a file, dipped quickly into a pot of zinc-chloride and its faces rubbed on a scrap of tinplate on which has been melted some soft-solder. When the surfaces are evenly covered with soft-solder, the bit is ready for use.

Cleaning and Fluxing of Work

It is necessary that the surfaces to be joined are absolutely clean and bright. They must then be evenly covered with zinc-chloride by means of a small cheap brush.

Heating of Soldering-bit

The soldering-bit must be heated in a soldering-stove to the correct heat, sufficiently hot to fuse the soft-solder very readily, but not so hot that its tinned surface is burnt off. The point of the bit is then rubbed on a block of sal-ammoniac to clean it.

Use of Soldering-bit

In commencing the operation, the fluxed soldering-bit is held on the work (which has been arranged level on a fire-brick or asbestos sheet), resting in contact long enough to allow the bit to raise the temperature of the metal, by conduction, to the melting-point of the solder. The solder-ing-bit is fed from the end of a thin stick of soft-solder and moved very slowly, without being lifted off, until the whole of the surface of the metal has been evenly tinned. The bit must be held at such an angle that the soft-solder will leave it easily and flow on to the metal being tinned. (A soldering-bit is not a paint-brush !) The correct amount of tinning is a matter of great importance. Too little will produce gaps in the final joint and an excess will flood out from the edges on to the surrounding surfaces when the joint is finally flushed.

Assembling

The parts of the joint are again fluxed and placed in even and thorough contact and secured in place, sometimes by thin, untinned soft iron bind-ing-wire, sometimes by weighting or by means of 2 inch iron split-pins, and occasionally their own weight is sufficient.

Flushing

A pencil blowpipe flame is used for heating, and is directed evenly round the joint until the soft-solder which is on one of the parts fuses (Plate 35, Fig. 2). If the joint has been made correctly, the soft-solder will appear as a thin line, without gaps or flooding, at the joint

7

edges. It is allowed to set and then scoured with fine pumice-powder and water to remove the waste flux.

(b) Loaded Joint

This is a joint between a surface and an edge, usually at right-angles, for example, the base of a bowl-mounting to its base-ring (Plate 35, Figs. 3 and 4).

The amount of soft-solder carried by a thin edge would not be sufficient to make a strong joint. The metal near the edge is therefore 'loaded' on its reverse side by an excess of soft-solder, part of which, when flushed by a blowpipe flame, flows by capillary attraction through the minute gap of the joint. The remainder is formed by surface tension into a concave buttress behind the joint, and when set adds very considerably to its strength. The main requirements are similar to the previous joint.

Loading

The part of the joint to be tinned in this instance is the one containng the edge. The metal surface immediately behind the edge of the joint is tinned more liberally than previously. It is held in pliers and turned so that the point of the soldering-bit can apply a fairly heavy coating of soft-solder round the work (Plate 35, Fig. 3). Small parts must not be heated by the soldering-bit so hot that the soft-solder already applied will melt off.

Assembling

An edge, the inside of which has been loaded, must be ground perfectly flat and care is needed to ensure the perfect contact of the parts of the joint by the securing methods previously suggested.

Flushing

The heating should be just sufficient to draw the soft-solder through to the front of the joint (Plate 35, Fig. 4). If further continued, more soft-solder may be drawn through than is required. This will also happen if the joint is badly fitted.

2. SINGLE-PROCESS SOFT-SOLDERING

By this method, particular joints are more easily made by one application of soft-solder. The foregoing general requirements apply, the difference being that the initial tinning or loading is dispensed with and the joint is made between two 'dry' or untinned surfaces. Here again, there are two very similar applications of the method, and many soft-soldered joints may be made by either, the choice being usually one of convenience.

(a) Pre-determined Application

As its name implies, the necessary amount of soft-solder is estimated. The method consists of fitting, cleaning, fluxing and assembling the un-tinned parts of the joint, which is then 'charged' with a sufficient number of small pieces or 'panels' of soft-solder cut from a thin stick which has been hammered out. The panels are applied with corn-tongs or tweezers at regular intervals and in such a position that the excess soft-solder, if any, can be easily removed.

Flushing

The work is heated with a blowpipe 'pencil' flame so that the panels of soft-solder fuse and are drawn through the joint, assisted by capillary attraction (Plate 36, Fig. 2).

This operation should make use of one of the most important principles in any blowpipe soldering. Molten solder will flow to the hottest part of the work and can be 'drawn' for surprising distances. Therefore the heat from the blowpipe must be applied to the work away from the soft-solder, i.e. on the opposite side of the joint, so that the soft-solder will be drawn through the joint. If the soft-solder panels are placed on the inside of a joint, the heat must be applied to the outside. If they are applied outside a joint then the inside must be heated (compare Figs. 1 and 2, Plate 36). A fair amount of even and general pre-heating of a job is, of course, necessary, but the small pencil flame which finally flushes the soft-solder should be applied to take advantage of the flow of the soft-solder to the hotter metal.

(b) Direct Application

By this method the soft-solder is fed directly from the thin stick to the untinned surfaces. Except for this difference, the previous general requirements are similar.

Flushing

The blowpipe is held in one hand and a stick of soft-solder in slide-tongs or pliers in the other. The work is pre-heated and then a small pencil flame is directed on to the joint.   The end of a hammered-out and fluxed soft-solder stick is touched on the joint just behind the flame.   If the joint is at the correct temperature the soft-solder will melt off the end of the stick easily and will run freely along the joint (Plate 36, Fig. 4, *a*). The flame is moved round the joint slowly and further applications of soft-solder made.   The flame must never be directed on to the end of the soft-solder stick.   If this happens, blobs will be rapidly melted off.   A small cheap brush, dipped in flux, can often be used with advantage to assist in the final even flushing, when sufficient soft-solder has been applied (Plate 36, Fig. 4, *b*).   Care is necessary to ensure that the soft-solder is applied only to the joint, and then not in excess, to prevent flooding on to the surrounding metal surfaces.

EXAMPLES OF SOFT-SOLDERED JOINTS

An example of a tinned joint is provided by the soldering of a circle of moulding to the base of a low hollowed tray.   In the assembly of the joint, three loops of binding-wire are passed round the tray with the ring in position.   Six pieces of ⅛ inch copper wire are cut to length and strained under the wire ties on to the circle of moulding, thus firmly securing the joint by pressure (Plate 35, Figs. 1 and 2).

A loaded joint is illustrated by the soft-soldering of a bowl-mounting to its base-ring (Plate 35, Figs. 3 and 4).

Sometimes a solid ball is used as a knob or as a foot.   It is gripped between pieces of wood in the vice and a small flat filed on it.   This is tinned and, when set, a small amount of the applied soft-solder filed off, again producing another flat, on which the ball sits (Plate 35, Fig. 5). It is soft-soldered to its lid by a pencil flame directed on to the ball only.

Hollowed feet have their edges tinned and a tiny nick filed in the edge on the inside of each foot to allow the heated air inside to expand during the flushing operation (Plate 35, Fig. 6).   The work is cooled in water after the flushing of each foot, so that it does not accumulate sufficient heat to fuse the joints of previously applied feet.

The jointing of a ring of moulding to a flat disc (Plate 36, Fig. 1), is an example of pre-determined application, as is also the soft-soldering of a small bowl-mounting (Plate 36, Fig. 2).

The jointing of a vase foot is an illustration of the method by which soft-solder may be drawn through a joint and then vertically upwards. A circle of moulding is silver-soldered to the base, and the body of the vase is soft-soldered in the recess so formed.   Panels of soft-solder are applied on the inside of the base, fused by a pencil blowpipe flame and drawn through the joint and then vertically to the top edge of the circle of moulding by capillary attraction (Plate 36, Fig. 3).

The soft-soldering of an applied wire edge is executed by the direct application of soft-solder from the stick, the end of which should be hammered out to a thin edge (Plate 36, Fig. 4, *a* and *b*).

CLEANING OFF SOFT-SOLDERED JOINTS

The utmost care should be taken to prevent an excess of applied soft-solder, the removal of which is an extremely tedious operation, and one which is capable of causing serious damage to surrounding surfaces.   The correct handling of a soft-soldered joint should produce a thin hairline of soft-solder at the edge of the flushed joint on the face of the work. More than that is waste, the removal of which takes a considerable time, due to a marked tendency of soft-solder to clog files, scrapers and any other tool employed in the cleaning off.

Excess soft-solder at the edge of a joint is removed with a bent scraper, which is pulled towards the worker.   It may also be removed with smooth safe-edged and other files, which should always be rubbed with chalk to minimize clogging.

Soft-soldered corded wires are cleaned off with fine steel or brass wire scratch-brushes.

Great care is required to prevent overheating by a blowpipe flame. In every case the flushing flame should consist of a small pencil flame only.   Soft-soldered work that has become thoroughly dirty by oxidation caused by overheating must be cooled, cleaned and refluxed before proceeding farther.

Should it become necessary to dismantle a joint, it should be lightly fluxed and heated and the uppermost part lifted off with pliers.   The previous application of soft-solder is removed with a small piece of folded rag, moistened with zinc-chloride, the heated parts being held in pliers.

A surface may be screened from the adherence of soft-solder by being painted with a thin paste of rouge and water.   If the required screening is close to a joint, there is a danger of the zinc-chloride flux mixing with the rouge and becoming fouled by it.   Under these circumstances the rouge should be mixed with a cellulose lacquer instead of water.

FAULTS

The causes of faulty joints are summarized:—

Faulty Tinning

Dirty surfaces.   Insufficient or dirty flux.   Underheating of soldering-bit.   Sheet metal soft-soldered while resting on a metallic surface, causing loss of heat by conduction.   Insufficient or excess soft-solder used. ' Paint-brush ' action of soldering-bit.

Gaps in Flushed Joint

Dirty surfaces.   Insufficient or dirty flux.   Insufficient soft-solder. Underheating.   Parts of joint not in close contact.   Insufficient ties. Overheating producing oxidation of surfaces.

Flooding

Surfaces excessively tinned.   Excess of applied soft-solder panels. Displaced soft-solder which floods over surfaces when fused.   Overheating of a loaded joint.   Parts of a loaded joint not in close contact.

Displaced Joint

Insufficient ties.   Accidental movement of work before cooling. Sudden heating causing uneven expansion.

CHOICE OF SOFT-SOLDERING METHOD

In early elementary work it is recommended that tinned and loaded joints, also the pre-determined method, are used until some skill in soft-soldered jointing is acquired.

Any later soft-soldered work should employ the direct application method wherever possible on account of its greater precision, and also that it gives valuable practice in the direct application of silver-solder.   It should be remembered that soft-soldering is a subsidiary jointing method, and that the direct application of silver-solder for all joints is the basic method, skill in which should be the final aim in the jointing operations of hammered metalwork.

CHAPTER XXIII

SILVER-SOLDERING

The Process—Silver-solder—Flux—Assembling Materials—Heating Equipment—Types of Silver-soldered Joint—Fitting of Silver-soldered Joints—Jointing Methods—Procedure—Pre-determined Application—Direct Application—Faults—Precautions and Safeguards—Examples of Silver-soldered Joints.

SILVER-SOLDERING is the basic jointing process of hammered metalwork and consists of the fusion of silver-solder with the surfaces of the joint. It may entirely replace soft-soldering in work in copper, gilding-metal and brass. Many of the requirements of soft-soldering are equally necessary in the process of silver-soldering, notably those demanding cleanliness in working and accuracy in fitting. The two processes are, however, entirely separate, having very wide differences.

Silver-soldering is a high-temperature process requiring red heat for the fusion of the silver-solder. Work that is silver-soldered in a final operation is therefore left in an annealed state.

Its joints are wonderfully strong, as tough as the metal they join if correctly made, so that work containing silver-soldered joints may be shaped by the hammer processes. It should always be the jointing process used in any work other than elementary.

The process is more difficult than soft-soldering, demanding a confidence in its execution acquired only after thoughtful practice. One of the most attractive features is its variety. Each silver-soldered joint (other than a few of the simple ones) must be approached as a fresh problem to be solved by a study of its own particular requirements and by careful attention to detail. It is certainly one of the most fascinating processes of the craft.

SILVER-SOLDER

Silver-solder is an alloy of silver and brass or silver and copper. It is graded according to the temperature at which it fuses, i.e. whether it is 'easy-running' or 'hard-running.'

If brass is used in the alloy it becomes easy-running and when copper

103

is contained it is hard-running. Most manufacturers produce several grades of varying melting-points, supplied in sheet, strip, filings, round and square wires of several gauges.

For ordinary work, two grades of silver-solder are necessary, a good-quality easy-running and also a hard-running grade. If sheet silver-solder is used it must be cut into small panels before it is applied (by one method). There is less trouble in cutting wire than sheet, also the wire lies closer to a joint than pieces of sheet metal.

Suitable gauges for silver-solder wire are Nos. 16 and 20 S.W.G.

The easy-running grade is used for all ordinary joints and the hard-running is required when it is desired, for some reason, to make subsequent joints without re-fusing the first, for which the hard-running grade would be used. The easy-running grade fuses and flushes a joint before the melting-point of the hard-running is reached.

The hard-running grade is also used on work which has to be heated many times. If easy-running silver-solder is used, the repeated firing volatilizes the zinc which is a constituent of the brass in easy-running silver-solder. The surface of the joint is then left rough and pitted, in addition to which the quality of the joint deteriorates at each firing, i.e. it becomes more brittle.

For silver-soldered work which is subsequently shaped by hammering, the toughness of the silver-solder is of first importance. Its hardness is of relatively little moment. The joints of such work must invariably be made with a good easy-running grade. Hard-running silver-solder is more brittle and will fracture before the simplest shaping operation is completed.

Flux

A flux to protect the surfaces of the joint from oxidation at high temperature is necessary. This is Borax, which, when fused, covers the joint with a protective glaze, excluding the air and thus preventing oxidation.

Borax is most conveniently used in the form of a hard moulded cone of finely ground powder. The base of the cone is rubbed on the rough surface of a small earthenware borax-tray, enough being ground off in water to produce a flux of thin creamy consistency.

It is applied with a small water-colour brush, sufficient being used to cover the surfaces. No useful purpose is served by using an excess, the fused glaze of which takes a considerable time to dissolve in acid when the work is finally pickled.

ASSEMBLING MATERIALS

The assembling and securing of a joint for silver-soldering is a very important operation which is made comparatively easy if the correct materials are available. The requirement is that the parts of the joint are secured in contact by being bound together with soft iron wire or held in position by iron split-pins. Three gauges of soft iron wire are necessary—Nos. 18, 20 and 22 S.W.G. It is important that the wire is neither tinned nor galvanized, as this would produce pitted lines round the work where it was in contact with the wire, due to the tin or zinc combining with the surface of the metal at high temperature.

A small piece of Nos. 24 or 26 S.W.G. soft copper sheet is also necessary, from which to cut small guards which are bent over a finished edge or corner on the work, to protect it from the tightened binding-wire that would cut into the metal, which is exceedingly soft when at red heat.

Suitable sizes for iron split-pins (cotter-pins) are 2 inches and 1 inch long and $\frac{1}{8}$ inch thick. One of the ends of each pin should be bent outwards before use to facilitate its application.

HEATING EQUIPMENT

A gas supply of $\frac{3}{8}$ inch diameter for small work and $\frac{1}{2}$ or $\frac{3}{4}$ inch for large work is desirable. It is connected to a blowpipe having separately controlled gas and air supply, so that the several types of flame required may be produced at will. Air-blast is required in the form of foot-bellows or a motor-driven blower. A soldering-hearth, preferably with a turntable on which work can be rotated, is also needed and a supply of whole and broken fire-brick with which to 'pack' a job on the hearth to conserve the heat.

TYPES OF SILVER-SOLDERED JOINT

Silver-soldered joints are in one of the following classes:—

(*a*) End-to-end joints (butt joint in wire or moulding. Plate 37, Fig. 2).

(*b*) Edge-to-edge joints (butt seam. Plate 37, Fig. 3).

(*c*) Edge-to-surface joints (Plate 37, Fig. 6).

(*d*) Surface-to-surface joints (Plate 38, Fig. 1).

FITTING OF SILVER-SOLDERED JOINTS

It is essential that the fit of any silver-soldered joint be as good as possible. The general methods suggested are described in Chapter XXI. The following particular methods of fitting should be noted.

Both ends of a butt joint in square, half-round, thick round wire or moulding should be nicked at right-angles with the edge of a half-round or triangular file, to ensure the entry of the molten silver-solder, which, in this instance, is usually the hard-running grade.

The edges of a butt seam should be finished with a rough file to form a key for the silver-solder. They must be in contact all along their length.

In edge-to-surface joints, the surface must first be made perfectly true and the edge then fitted to it, usually by grinding or flatting.

The requirement of surface-to-surface joints is that both faces are true and are in even contact throughout the joint.

SILVER-SOLDERING METHODS

As in soft-soldering, the jointing methods of silver-soldering differ chiefly in the way in which the silver-solder is applied to the joint :—

1. PRE-DETERMINED APPLICATION

Joint charged with cut pieces or panels of silver-solder (Plate 37, Fig. 1).

2. DIRECT APPLICATION

Joint fed directly from silver-solder wire or strip (Plate 37, Fig. 2).

PROCEDURE

The requirements of both the foregoing methods are given:—

1. PRE-DETERMINED APPLICATION

This method of making a silver-soldered joint is a simple one, and in early work is likely to give more certain results.

Checking

The joint surfaces are brought together and their fitting finally checked.

Fluxing

Borax flux is evenly applied to the surfaces of the joint with a water-colour brush.

Tying-up

Ties of iron binding-wire (and guards to finished edges) are arranged in position. Loops must be left in the wire on each side of a job so that the wire tension can be equalized. (This may also be accomplished by the formation of Z-shaped kinks in the binding-wire made with flat-nosed pliers). The wire and loops are finally tightened so that even contact is maintained between the joint surfaces. In other cases, iron split-pins at frequent and regular intervals are used.

Re-checking

The joint should be examined for final fit and location, to ensure that the binding-wire or pins have not caused displacement.

Charging

Silver-solder wire is cut into short lengths and fluxed by being immersed in the borax-tray. They are taken out with corn-tongs or tweezers, applied to the joint and pushed close against internal angles, if any. If the joint is curved, the silver-solder wire should be pulled through thumb and finger to make it conform to the curve before it is cut up. It will then lie close to the internal angle of the joint.

Packing-up

The work is placed level on the soldering-hearth and 'packed-up' from the floor of the hearth on pieces of fire-brick. Sometimes a large, closely-packed and tangled mass of thin iron wire is used for this purpose. Whole or half fire-bricks are then placed round it to conserve the heat.

Heating

The heat must be applied in three separate and distinct stages :—

(*a*) *Evaporating Flame.*—A small soft blowpipe flame is first applied to evaporate the moisture in the borax and to harden it.

(*b*) *Pre-heating Flame.*—A large soft flame is next used with which to slowly and evenly heat the whole of the work to a dull-red heat. During this stage a pointed length of thick untinned iron wire or thin rod should be available with which to replace silver-solder that may have been moved by the expansion of the flux.

(*c*) *Flushing Flame*.—A hard flame is now directed on to the joint away from the silver-solder to flush the joint, drawing the molten silver-solder through it to the region of the hotter metal.   Immediately this happens the flame is removed.

Cooling

The packing-up should be removed and the work allowed to lose all its red heat.   It is quenched in water, the binding-wire and pins removed and finally placed in a pickle-bath to dissolve the fused borax.

The binding-wire may be sometimes inadvertently silver-soldered to the work.   The wire should then be gripped in small round-nosed pliers as near to the point of adhesion as possible and turned off by slowly rotating the pliers.   In certain cases it may be necessary to file it away to prevent damage to the work.

2. Direct Application

Silver-soldering by this method is the basic jointing operation of the craft.   Speed, precision in working and a cleanliness of finish are its chief merits.   It is admittedly more difficult, especially in the early stages of the work, and it is recommended that practice is persisted in until complete confidence is obtained, so that any ordinary silver-soldered joint may be made by direct application.

The preliminary fitting, tying-up and general requirements are exactly similar to the pre-determined method, the only point of difference being that the prepared joint is not charged with pieces of silver-solder wire.

Silver-solder in thin, narrow strip or heavy-gauge wire (Nos. 20 to 16 S.W.G.) is used and is gripped in a pin-vice or in slide-tongs and boraxed.   When wire is used, the end of a length is passed through the hollow handle of a pin-vice, allowing 2 or 3 inches to project through the jaws.   (The remainder is slid through the hollow handle as required.)

The work is thoroughly pre-heated with a large soft flame, and when the mass of metal surrounding the joint is at an even red heat, the end of the silver-solder strip or wire is applied to the joint.   Its point of application should be just behind, but not in contact with the blowpipe flame, the air-blast of which has been increased to produce a hard flame for the flushing of the joint. Silver-solder will fuse from the end of the wire, partly by its contact with the red-hot metal and partly by radiation from the blowpipe flame. It will be realized that the area of metal immediately under the flame will be hotter than the point at which the silver-solder is applied. As the silver-solder fuses, it will, therefore, run under the flame to the region of hotter metal, assisted by capillary attraction. The silver-solder wire is slowly and evenly fed into the joint, keeping the fusing end in contact until sufficient has entered the joint to flush the small area dealt with. When an evenly flushed joint has ' run ' for perhaps a distance of $1\frac{1}{2}$ inches, the blowpipe flame is moved and a fresh application of silver-solder made, the operation being repeated until the joint is finished. It is important to ensure that the pre-heating is adequate. If the surrounding metal is not sufficiently hot, the applied silver-solder will not run, but will melt off and remain on the metal, probably becoming oxidized. Neither must the silver-solder come into direct contact with the blowpipe flame. When this happens, the intense heat applied to such a small mass of metal will immediately fuse the end of the wire into a large grain or bead or, in an extreme case, a portion of the wire will be completely melted off.

FAULTS

It is always wise to examine any unsuccessful joints so that the cause of failure is known.

Gaps in Joint

Dirty surfaces. Insufficient flux. Dirty flux. Insufficient silver-solder. Underheating, leaving some applied silver-solder not thoroughly fused. Unequal heating of parts of joint, causing silver-solder to run away from joint. Joint not in close contact. Insufficient ties. Burnt-out ties.

Displaced Joint

Accidental movement of work at red heat. Insufficient ties. Burnt-out ties. Sudden heating, causing unequal expansion. Part of joint not annealed after shaping process, causing movement when heated. Fusing and movement of previously made joint.

Flooding

Excess silver-solder. Unequal heating of parts of joint, causing silver-solder to run to one part. Displaced silver-solder, which floods on to surface of work when fused.

Uneven Joint Surfaces

Insufficient flux. Over-firing of easy-running silver-solder, causing pitting. Underheating. Premature application of silver-solder (in direct method).

Damaged Metal Surfaces

Soft-solder previously on work. Soft-solder picked up from soldering-hearth or fire-brick. Unguarded binding-wire, causing cutting of edges and corners. Overheating, causing partial fusion of surfaces of work. Scratches made by split-pins carelessly applied.

Distortion of Work

Sudden quenching at high temperature, causing uneven contraction. Sudden heating, causing uneven expansion.

PRECAUTIONS AND SAFEGUARDS

The secret of success in the making of the more advanced silver-soldered joints lies in careful attention to detail, much of which must be considered before the actual heating operation. Precautions taken then will prevent any very serious trouble when the work as at red heat and therefore extremely difficult to handle. The more important points in this connection are suggested :—

Clean Surfaces

The surfaces of a joint must be thoroughly clean before the application of the flux. Borax is not a cleaning agent.

Sufficient Flux

It is necessary that enough borax is applied to form an adequate surface of glaze over the whole of the joint. A very slightly greasy surface will not take an even covering of borax, and must be scoured with pumice-powder and water. In work containing more than one joint, it is essential that all the joints to be silver-soldered are fluxed before the work is heated, even if only one of the joints is being made at the time, e.g. the four corners of a folded rectangular box which are flushed separately.

Clean Flux

The presence of impurities in applied flux will hinder, if not prevent, its action.

Sufficient Ties

When assembling a joint, it is necessary to ensure that enough ties are provided to hold not only the joint being silver-soldered but to support others previously silver-soldered. The spring-compression of a new split-pin must not be relied upon to secure a joint tightly. It will be non-existent at red heat. New split-pins should be annealed before use.

Damage by Ties

Considerable damage can be caused to sharp corners and finished edges by binding-wire, which rapidly cuts into the metal when it is soft at red heat. It can be easily prevented by arranging guards consisting of small pieces of very thin copper, under the ties where they are likely to cause trouble. On no account must zinc, tinplate or tinned copper be used for this purpose.

Loss of Heat by Radiation

A good deal of gas and time are wasted if work is openly exposed during a heating operation, as much of the heat is then lost by radiation. It should be surrounded with fire-brick to conserve the heat as much as possible. If this matter is attended to, it is possible to silver-solder large work with a surprisingly small flame.

Loss of Heat by Conduction

In the silver-soldering of any part of a joint forming a base, it is necessary to raise it from the soldering-hearth to prevent loss of heat by conduction to the hearth. Small pieces of broken fire-brick will support large work, and short lengths of binding-wire or broken piercing-saws will sufficiently raise small work from the surface of a fire-brick. If this precaution is not taken, parts of the work will be overheated and possibly fused before the base is sufficiently hot.

Protection of Previous Joints

Jeweller's rouge, mixed into a paste with water, should be applied to previously made joints to protect them from the heat of a later joint. It will not prevent the silver-solder from fusing. It merely prevents it running. Therefore rouge cannot be relied upon to support even a small part which is likely to move when at red heat, and such a part must be tied with binding-wire to secure it.

Immersion in sulphuric-acid pickle should immediately follow any silver-soldering operation so that the fused borax is removed. This is particularly necessary for work containing more than one silver-soldered joint. Fused borax on a previously made joint will again act as a flux in a subsequent heating, possibly causing the first joint to fuse unevenly.

Sufficient Silver-solder

Whilst an excess of silver-solder should be avoided, sufficient must be applied adequately to flush a joint. The difference in the amount required to flush a butt seam and that required for the application of a flat moulding of an equal length is considerable.

Direction of Flow of Molten Silver-solder

Advantage must always be taken of the fact that molten silver-solder will flow to the region of the hotter metal. Joints should be assembled and heat for flushing applied with that consideration in view.

Even Heating

A large pre-heating flame should always be applied if it is available so that the whole of the work is heated evenly. A smaller flame must be moved slowly over the surfaces for the same purpose. Sudden local heating may produce distortion by uneven expansion and a joint may be displaced.

Unequal Heating

Silver-soldered joints composed of a large and small part demand special treatment. Before flushing, the parts are not in close metallic contact. A film of dried borax, which is a poor conductor of heat, separates them. If they are treated equally, the small part which is heated rapidly cannot lose its heat by conduction to the larger mass, as it would do if they were in metallic contact. The small part will be overheated and may fuse before the large part is at red heat, or the silver-solder will fuse and rush to the small hotter part, flooding over its surface. Work of this kind must, therefore, be heated unequally by directing the flame to the larger mass or by screening the smaller one with asbestos sheet. Small exposed parts not being actually jointed may be protected by being painted with rouge.

Silver-soldering Small Wires

For similar reasons, the silver-soldering of applied corded and thin wires demands special consideration. If the work and the wire are heated equally, one of two things will happen. The silver-solder may fuse and rush to the wire, filling up the twists or flooding over its surface, or the wire will expand outwards away from the body of the work between the split-pins or ties. The correct treatment is to heat the wire by conduction. The flame should be directed on the body of the work only, the wire being heated by conduction from it.

Overheating

Only sufficient heat thoroughly to flush a joint should be given. An excess may produce overheating, causing partial fusion of the surfaces which may not be apparent during the operation. When cooled, the surfaces are found to be rough and pitted. Easy-running silver-solder should be used wherever suitable, so that the risk of overheating is minimized.

Observation of Heating Progress

It is always wise to remove the flame for a second or so at intervals in the heating of a silver-soldered joint so that the heat of the work can be seen more clearly. This is a valuable aid in the even heating of a joint, and may prevent the partial fusion of a small part, the overheating of which may be unnoticed under the flame.

Silver-soldering in Strong Light

If metal is heated in a strong light it will appear much cooler than it really is, which may be the cause of accidental overheating. This is especially true of silver and brass. There is little apparent change in the colour of silver at red heat, and some grades of brass have a dangerously low fusing-point. Silver-soldering should never be done in sunlight or in any strong light.

Burnt-out Ties

Occasionally exposed ties of binding-wire burn out. This is frequently not the calamity it might appear to be. By the time any wire tie has fused, the work will have been thoroughly annealed and any existing tension or strain relieved. Unless it is obvious that a faulty joint will be produced, the work should continue. It is often possible to squeeze a

8

part into contact momentarily with light tongs or pliers, or by light pressure with a thin iron rod, thus saving much labour in cooling, cleaning and re-assembly.

Preliminary Annealing

Parts of a joint which have been shaped by hammering in a previous operation should be annealed before being silver-soldered. If this is not done, the metal, being internally strained, may move when heated, due to the relief of the strain. This may displace the joint or spoil its good alignment.

Built-up Work

Silver-soldered work built up from a number of parts should neither be heated nor quenched suddenly. It is essential to avoid distortion due to violent expansion and contraction.

Use of Hard-running Silver-solder

Small built-up units, e.g. handle sockets, which have later to be jointed to larger parts, should be silver-soldered with hard-running silver-solder. This avoids awkward tying-up when the final joint is made with easy-running silver-solder, as the heat required will not be sufficient to fuse the first joints.

In other cases, particularly when hard-running silver-solder is used (which is not damaged by repeated firing), it may be desirable to allow previously made joints to run when subsequent joints are made. The work must be securely tied and previous joints re-fluxed to ensure that they fuse and run evenly.

EXAMPLES OF SILVER-SOLDERED JOINTS

Examples are given illustrating the arrangement of the more common silver-soldered joints. In the making of every joint, the final flushing flame is the important one. For that reason it is the one illustrated in the sketches. It should be imagined that the work has been heated to a dull red and that the flame shown is the smaller hard one which finally flushes the joint, and also that the fire-brick packing-up extends right round each job. In some cases the work would be arranged on a turn-table.

The method of pre-determined application is illustrated in certain cases to enable the work in early stages to be simplified. Direct application is possible in every case and should be the ultimate aim.

Butt Joint in Strip (Plate 37, Fig. 1)

This is probably the simplest silver-soldered joint. Very little silver-solder is required.

Butt Joint in Square Wire (Plate 37, Fig. 2)

The binding-wire should be fairly thin to facilitate its application. The joint may have a tiny piece of silver-solder applied, or it may be touched with silver-solder wire when at full-red heat.

Seam in Cylinder (Plate 37, Fig. 3)

This is a joint that is often required and one that should give no trouble if the fitting and tying-up are carefully done. When arranging, a small space should be left between the work and the rear fire-brick to allow the free passage of air so that the flame is not choked.

Seam in Cone (Plate 37, Fig. 4)

A similar joint to the cylinder, except that it requires special tying-up. Two or three vertical wires are arranged with either loops or kinks at suitable points in their length. The ends are looped over the top and base of the cone. The horizontal ties are then applied, the loops or kinks preventing them from sliding down the taper of the cone.

Moulding to Flat Sheet (Plate 37, Fig. 5)

In this and similar joints, split-pins are used for tying-up. The work should be examined before firing to ensure that biased pressure of the pins has not lifted the far edge of the moulding away from the sheet. In narrow strip, the pins would be applied alternately from each edge to equalize the pressure.

Ring to Flat Sheet (Plate 37, Fig. 6)

The silver-solder is applied to a margin which may or may not be waste. It is not good practice to allow exposed wire ties to cross the work. In this case, however, the required heat would not be sufficient to fuse them unless hard-running silver-solder is used. Thicker binding-wire would then be used, hooked over the edge of the ring instead of crossing the upper surface of the work.

Overlay Joint (Plate 38, Fig. 1)

This is an example of a surface-to-surface joint in which small pieces of silver-solder are fused through the joint.

Butt Joint in Wire or Moulding (Plate 38, Fig. 2)

This is normally a very awkward joint.   It is made easy by the use of a wire-soldering cramp made from spring-calipers.   The ends of the wire are secured in a joint-tool, filed square, removed and inserted in the cramp. They are then fluxed and brought together by tightening the cramp.   In the case of thin wire, the ends are heated by a pencil flame and touched when red hot as lightly as possible with thin silver-solder wire, the end of which has been flattened.   When dealing with thicker wire or mouldings the procedure is simpler.   A very tiny piece of silver-solder wire is fluxed and screwed up between the ends of the moulding in the cramp. The joint is then simply heated.   As the silver-solder fuses, its space is instantly closed by the existing slight end-pressure of the cramp.

Handle to Lid (Plate 38, Fig. 3)

Thick binding-wire is looped in the handle and passed over the lid and hooked to the edges.   Two other loops are also included to obtain an even wire tension, in order that the handle may be easily adjusted to a vertical position.

Bowl-mounting (Plate 38, Fig. 4)

The silver-solder may be either internally applied or fed from a wire or strip.   Heavy-gauge binding-wire is necessary.

Recessed Base (Plate 38, Fig. 5)

This is an example of a simple joint which requires elaborate tying-up. The base must be accurately fitted and not forced into place.   Adequate guards for the corners and edges are required, those over the base being arranged as stops to prevent twisting and distortion of the base.   Very even heating is also necessary.

Flush Base (Plate 38, Fig. 6)

In these joints it is easier to arrange matters so that the base projects slightly as a waste margin.   Slots are cut, the metal of which, when bent up, prevents distortion of the cylinder by acting as stops.   The really import-ant requirement in this type of joint is the packing-up of the base from the floor of the soldering-hearth.   The silver-solder is applied on the inside and flushed through.   It may be also directly fed from strip to the outside.

Spout Joint (Plate 39, Fig. 1)

This provides an excellent example of the silver-soldering of unequal masses of metal, also of the comparatively rare instances in which a joint requires no tying. The joint is arranged level, the spout and body boraxed and adjusted whilst damp. A little gum tragacanth may be added when the borax is ground to form an adhesive. When the flux is dry the silver-solder is applied and the work heated slowly and unequally so that the spout is not overheated.

Handle Joint (Plate 39, Fig. 2)

This is an arrangement in which two joints are flushed separately. They are both fluxed and tied and the whole of the work heated. One joint is then flushed by direct application of silver-solder, then the work is reversed and the other joint flushed by the same method.

Applied Moulding (Plate 39, Figs. 3 and 4)

Two methods are shown, the first being the usual one. The second takes advantage of a convenient recess in which to apply the silver-solder. In neither case is the flushing flame directed on to the moulding. The first method is a good example of heating a wire or moulding by conduction from a larger mass of metal.

Handle Mounting or Socket (Plate 39, Fig. 5)

The complete socket is fired in three stages with hard-running silver-solder. This is not the only arrangement, but it dispenses with awkward tying-up.

Plaster Cramp (Plate 39, Fig. 6)

Frequently in repair work a butt joint occurs which defeats all attempts at tying-up by the usual methods. An example is included as an illustration of one method of overcoming the difficulty. A mixture of 1 part plaster-of-paris and 2 parts of sand is made and placed in a simple mould —a cardboard box, for instance. The joint is arranged and set in the plaster and is then very thoroughly dried in a slow oven or stove. The mould is broken away and the work placed on the soldering-hearth and silver-soldered in the usual way. When cool, it is immersed in water, the sand causing immediate disintegration of the plaster.

Insets

It is occasionally necessary to insert a patch as a repair in order to remove a serious blemish. A case in point would be a small pitted hole caused by accidental contact of soft-solder when the work is red hot. The blemish should be completely removed by drilling, filing or saw-piercing and the sides of the hole so formed bevelled outwards with a round file to about 70 degrees. An inset of a thicker gauge of similar metal is filed to shape and bevelled to fit the hole, so that it is exactly flush on its lower surface, its bevelled sides preventing it from falling through. It is then tied in position and silver-soldered. The difference in thickness which appears on its upper surface is removed in cleaning off the completed inset with smooth files.

CHAPTER XXIV

HINGING

Types of Hinge—An Applied Hinge—A Stop-hinge—Drawn Hinge-tube.

HINGES are generally in one of two groups, either those constructed separately and applied as a final operation or those built up with the work as it proceeds. Some hinges permit of movement through their full range of opening, whilst in others the movement is limited by stops which support the weight of a lid.

On a teapot, or similar example, such a stop is often not necessary. The contact of the knob on the lid with the handle when the lid is open may limit the range of opening of the hinge, the handle forming a support for the lid in that position.

The design may be such that damage is avoided if a knob is prevented from coming into contact with another part. Boxes usually require a stop to prevent the lid from falling too far over when open, and the construction of such work may demand that the lid is only allowed to open just past its vertical position. In these instances a stop-hinge is fitted.

An example of each type is given:—

AN APPLIED HINGE

A simple method of construction of this type of hinge makes use of $\frac{1}{8}$ inch (or less) solid-drawn tubing having a thick wall.

The first stage is to silver-solder lengths of this tube to No. 16 or 18 S.W.G. metal, the edge of which has been bevelled to receive the side of the tube (Plate 40, Fig. 1). (Hard-running silver-solder is used for this joint.) The two pieces may be silver-soldered in one operation, either end to end or side by side, being afterwards separated with a brass-back saw (Plate 40, Fig. 2). The joint is cleaned off and the knuckles are then very accurately set out.

They are cut with a brass-back saw, the waste being removed with a special file which does not cut metal from the sides of the knuckles during the operation (Plate 40, Fig. 3). It is easily made by grinding the teeth from both faces of a 6 inch flat, smooth file, the waste metal being removed by the edge of the file only. The knuckles are carefully fitted together and a hard wire hinge-pin inserted (Plate 40, Figs. 4 and 5). It must be a good fit in the tube, and it is sometimes necessary to draw down a piece of thicker wire in a round drawplate, in order to obtain a satisfactory fit (Plate 33, Fig. 4).

The hinge is then cleaned off and finished to size, the waste which was allowed for ease of handling being cut away with a brass-back saw. A hinge of this type may be applied either opened horizontally or closed vertically, as the construction of the work demands, the side with the fewer knuckles being fitted to the lid (Plate 40, Fig. 6, *a* and *b*). Easy-running silver-solder should be used for the final jointing and at the completion of the fitting the hinge-pin may be inserted and cut flush, or a very small rounded-off projection left at each end.

An alternative construction consists of filing each half of the hinge from the solid, drilling for the hinge-pin and then filing and fitting the knuckles.

A BUILT-UP STOP-HINGE

The making of this type of hinge must be considered in its relation to a particular job and for that purpose a simple application to a small box is described (Plate 60). The first hinging operation commences when the box is jointed and the lid parted from the body. Its edges are ground flat and checked when placed together. A bevel is filed on each of the hinging edges which forms a groove when the body and lid are placed together and held very lightly in the vice.

Two pieces of rectangular strip for hinge-bearers, just longer than the box, are prepared and flatted. Their width should be $\frac{3}{32}$ inch and their thickness $\frac{1}{16}$ inch. A length of $\frac{1}{8}$ inch diameter tube with a thick wall is now placed in the groove made by the two filed bevels and the bearers placed in position edgewise, one on each side. Their location is accurately marked with a scriber (Plate 41, Fig. 1). They are then pinned on the body and lid and silver-soldered separately.

The next stage consists of checking their height, because upon the height of these hinge-bearers the angle of opening of the final hinge will depend, which should be just more than a right-angle. This is tested by placing the tube in position and holding the lid and body open so that the hinge-bearers are in contact with the tube correctly placed. Should they be too high they must now be filed on their top edges, care being taken to keep them accurately parallel, i.e. of even height.

Some rouge is mixed with cellulose lacquer to a very thin paste, and the whole of the box edges and all of the hinge-bearers except their top edges are very carefully painted with it and allowed to dry (Plate 41, Fig. 2). The tube is cut into five lengths, waste being left on the two end pieces. Their ends are carefully squared in a joint-tool and any inside burr removed by twisting a small drill on the end of the hole. The rouged box and lid are now held lightly in a vice and the tube assembled between the hinge-bearers. The ends of each tube are carefully and lightly rouged and placed in line between the hinge-bearers. A temporary hinge-pin of iron wire is inserted in the tubes and it must be an easy fit.

The box is removed from the vice and carefully tied up with binding-wire, protecting the corners with angle-strips of thin copper. The joints between the upper hinge-bearer and the first, third and fifth tubes are lightly rouged. The joints between the lower hinge-bearer and the second and fourth tubes are rouged and the whole allowed to dry. The joints between the upper hinge-bearer and the second and fourth tubes are boraxed. The joints between the lower hinge-bearer and the first, third and fifth tubes are boraxed and allowed to dry. The borax is applied thinly and must not be allowed to trespass on to the rouge. A small piece of silver-solder wire is applied to each boraxed joint and the whole of the joints fired at the same time (Plate 41, Fig. 3). It is, of course, essential that only sufficient silver-solder is applied, and it is wise to err on the side of too little. More can be added and re-fired, but if too much is used the moving parts of the hinge may be silver-soldered together. If desired, the silver-solder may be only partially flushed at the first firing, sufficient silver-solder being applied to 'tack' each tube to its appropriate bearer. The box may be then separated and the lid and body re-fired separately to complete the flushing.

The remaining operations consist of the removal of waste, cleaning off and the fitting of the final hinge-pin of hard wire.

DRAWN HINGE-TUBE

Hinge-tube (called Chenier) may be made from a parallel strip of sheet metal. Its width should be three times the diameter of the required tube.

The first stage, after annealing, consists of cutting one end to a long taper.   The strip is then worked U-shaped in a semicircular groove filed across a steel or iron block about $1\frac{1}{2}$ inches wide, or in a suitable groove in a tinman's crease-iron.   The end of the strip rests over the groove and a piece of steel wire is malleted on to it, depressing the strip into the groove.   The strip is moved along the groove until the other end is reached.   The edges are further closed and the tapered end may now be inserted into a large hole in a circular drawplate and drawn through that and progressively smaller holes until the edges are tightly closed.   Frequent annealing is necessary and it is also desirable to draw the tube on to a tallowed wire in order to keep it a good shape.   It is removed by reversing the drawplate in the vice and drawing it through a hole which will admit the wire but not the tube.

Hinge-tube of this kind must always be arranged in such a position that its open seam may be silver-soldered when the final joint to the hinge-bearers is made.

CHAPTER XXV

TREATMENT OF EDGES

The Reinforcing of Edges—Methods—Procedure in Edge-folding—Folding Straight Edges—Folding Edges of Rectangles and Polygons—Folding Curved Vertical Edges—Procedure in Edge-wiring—Wiring Straight Edges—Wiring Edges of Polygons—Wiring Curved Vertical Edges—Wiring Curved Horizontal Edges—Applied Wires—Mouldings—Corded Wires—Plaited Wire Bands.

EXCEPT in examples of the simplest hammered work, and then only when the diameter is small, may an edge be left free or unsupported. A thin free edge gives an unpleasant sense of flimsiness and non-rigidity when handled. In addition, an unsupported edge is weak constructionally, as the work will not keep its true shape in use.

To provide the necessary strength, unwarrantably thick metal would have to be used, to the detriment of the delicacy and lightness of the work, so that some form of edge-strengthening is necessary.

The chief requirement in the reinforcing of an edge is that strength is added without apparent weight. Heavy and cumbrous edges destroy refinement of proportion in the work as a whole.

The metal edges requiring special treatment are those at the extremities of a piece of hammered work. Those occurring intermediately are dealt with in the construction. They may be 'thrown-out' to receive another member or contracted to form a turned-down rim or fillet. They are important in the design of the work as a whole inasmuch as their incorrect treatment produces errors of balance and proportion. Their very position, however, precludes any possibility of leaving them unsupported, so that bases, rims and upper edges are the parts requiring consideration.

Bases usually present no particular problem. The requirements of strength and the protection of a sheet-metal edge used in the construction of mountings are met by the provision of a base-ring of square wire, moulding or rectangular strip. More latitude regarding weight is permissible in the base, and it is chiefly a matter to be dealt with in the normal construction of the work rather than by the application of a special process.

METHODS

In the case of outer edges of plates, trays and salvers and upper edges of bowls, the position is entirely different and methods of support involving one of the following processes must be used:—

1. EDGE FOLDING

Probably the simplest and most effective method of giving rigidity to an edge where great strength is not required is by folding the edge back over itself, forming a double metal-thickness. The more rounded the actual fold is, the stronger will be the edge.

2. EDGE WIRING

Where greater strength and rigidity are required, a wire is inserted and enclosed in a formed groove.

3. APPLIED WIRES AND MOULDINGS

The usual method of reinforcing an edge by the application of wires, which may be soft- or silver-soldered in one of several forms:—

Square, rectangular or half-round wire.
Drawn moulding.
Corded wire and plaited wire.

PROCEDURE IN EDGE FOLDING (Plate 42, Fig. 1)

There are four operations in edge folding:—

(a) Setting-out of folding allowance.
(b) Folding the edge to a right-angle.
(c) Folding the right-angle to 45 degrees.
(d) Closing the edge.

These stages are passed through in the folding of either straight or curved edges, though the method is different.

FOLDING STRAIGHT EDGES

The edge is trued up and filed smooth and the folding allowance marked off. Stage (a).

Stage (b) is executed in folding-bars or on a flat stake with a mallet. The third stage (c) is folded over the edge of a tinman's hatchet stake or similar bevelled edge (Plate 42, Fig. 2, c).

The final operation, stage (*d*), consists of closing the edge on a flatting-block with a light mallet, keeping the fold as full and rounded as possible (Plate 42, Fig. 2, *d*).

FOLDED EDGES OF RECTANGLES AND POLYGONS

When folding the edges of rectangles and regular polygons, it becomes necessary to estimate (Plate 6, Fig. 12) and remove the waste metal at the corners before the process can commence. The folding allowance on each side of the polygon is turned down to a right-angle on a flat stake, the length of the edge of which must be slightly less than the side of the polygon. The work is then inverted on a flatting-block and the folding allowance closed on to the face of the metal with a mallet, leaving the actual fold as rounded as possible. The finished corners are silver-soldered.

FOLDED CURVED VERTICAL EDGES

This operation is more difficult and requires some practice before the necessary precision is obtained.

Two inside height-lines are set out. The first is the height of the finished folded edge and the second is this height plus the folding allowance. It is also necessary to allow about $\frac{1}{16}$ inch waste, which is not removed at this stage. The annealed edge is turned with a hammer or mallet over the very slightly rounded edge of a flat stake or heavy bar, stage (*a*) (Plate 42, Fig. 3, *a*). The aim should be to stretch the metal over by tension rather than by compression, so that the tool must strike the extreme edge in glancing blows whilst the work is slowly rotated. During this operation the lower height-line on the inside of the work must be kept constantly over the edge of the stake or bar. A hammer is more precise than a mallet, but will cause much damage if handled carelessly.

The edge is then flatted over by lowering the angle of the work, stage (*b*) (Plate 42, Fig. 3, *b*), and care must be taken not to thin or over-hammer the edge. The circular form is re-trued on a suitable dome or ball stake to correct any slight distortion which the flatting of the edge may have produced. The correct width of the folding allowance is now marked out with spring-dividers which are set to this width, one point of which is slid along the inside edge, the other scribing a line on the horizontal rim. The waste is removed with shears and the edge filed up and finished with emery-cloth.

A flat narrow tracer or punch must be prepared, with a rounded-over edge (Plate 50, Fig. 1), and the rim turned down to 45 degrees, using the tracer in the vice, stage (*c*) (Plate 42, Fig. 3, *c*).

The final operation consists of closing the edge on a suitable stake, keeping the corner as full and rounded as possible, stage (*d*) (Plate 42, Fig. 3, *d*). A guard of scrap metal may be used, if a hammer is employed with which to protect the surfaces.

It is necessary that any hammer work be as light as possible to avoid thinning. Skill is required in this process in working very accurately to the lower height-line in the first folding operation. If this is not accurate, the final top edge will be wavy.

PROCEDURE IN EDGE-WIRING (Plate 43, Fig. 1)

The operations of edge-wiring are a continuation of those of edge-folding:—

(*a*) Setting-out of wiring allowance.
(*b*) Folding to right-angle.
(*c*) Folding right-angle to 45 degrees.
(*d*) Folding wiring allowance parallel.
(*e*) Insertion of the wire.
(*f*) Enclosing the wire.
(*g*) Closing the edge of the metal.
(*h*) Setting down, when the wired edge is required to be completely raised, as in the case of the horizontal edges of trays, plates and salvers.

There are several applications of the wired edge, three of the most common being:—

1. Straight wired edges.
2. Curved vertical wired edges.
3. Curved horizontal wired edges.

WIRING STRAIGHT EDGES

The operation proceeds as in folding straight edges until stage (*c*) is completed. The next stage, (*d*), consists of turning the wiring allowance still farther until it is parallel with the face of the metal. A flat piece of metal slightly thicker than the wire to be used is held up against the internal corner of the wiring allowance, which is then lightly malleted on to the piece of metal, forming a groove of even width, into which the wire will enter easily. The wire is inserted in the groove, stage (*e*), and enclosed with a mallet on a flatting-block, stage (*f*).

The edge is completely closed by means of a well-fitting grooving-tool (Plate 50, Fig. 4) and hammer on a flatting-block, stage (g) (Plate 43, Fig. 2). The sharp corners of the grooving-tool must be removed and its face, which may be very slightly convex with advantage, should be polished to prevent damage to the surfaces.

If the closed edge is required on an under surface, the wired edge being a raised one, as it frequently is, then the completed wired edge is " set down " by means of a setting-down tool and hammer on a flatting-block, stage (h) (Plate 43, Fig. 2). The special tool consists of a flat tapered point, very slightly curved on its working face to prevent damage by its corners and slightly bevelled on its working edge so that damage is not caused by its rear edge (Plate 50, Fig. 2). Care must be taken to ensure that its edge is not sharp enough to cut, nor that it is allowed to indent the metal during its use. The hammer blows must be eased off when the metal is brought into contact with the block, so that the work is not compressed between tool and block.

Wired Edges of Polygons

In the wiring of edges of rectangles, polygons and similar shapes, slightly differing methods must be used, depending upon whether the corners are sharp or rounded.

When the corners are sharp, waste metal must first be removed from the corners of the wiring allowance with a piercing-saw. (It will not be a straight-sided cut as for folded corners, but will take the form of a concave-sided waste removal which will allow the adjacent edges of the wiring allowance to meet evenly when the wire is enclosed.)

The wiring allowance is turned to a right-angle and then a length of the wire to be used is bent to a frame (with very sharp, well-defined corners) which exactly fits inside the turned wiring allowance. The waste ends of the wire are cut and fitted and the frame of wire is enclosed by malleting the wiring allowance over it, finally truing with a light hammer. If this wired edge is to be raised, the final operation is executed with a setting-down tool as previously described.

When the corners of wired polygons are rounded, the procedure is similar except that no waste removal at the corners is necessary. The straight part of the wiring allowance is turned and the rounded corner turned down by stretching on the squared and polished end of a short length of round bar held vertically in the vice, using a light hammer. The radius of the bar should equal that of the required rounded corner and the sharp edge of the end of the bar must be removed to prevent damage to the surfaces near the wired edge.

Wiring Curved Vertical Edges

The commencing operations are similar to the first two of the folding of a curved vertical edge, stages (*a*) and (*b*) (Plate 42, Fig. 3).

Stage (*c*) is also similar except that the thickness of the end of the tracer (Plate 50, Fig. 1) used for turning the edge must be very slightly greater than that of the wire being used.

The next step is the insertion of the wire, commencing at its centre and working first towards one end and then to the other, closing the edge sufficiently to secure the wire, which must lie evenly at the base of the groove, stage (*e*) (Plate 43, Fig. 3, *e*).

The edge is then closed with a mallet as far as possible, the ends of the wire cut, inserted and the remainder of the edge closed and trued up, stage (*f*) (Plate 43, Fig. 3, *f*).

The last stage (*g*) is the tucking-in, or finally closing the edge of the metal up to the surface of the work. This is executed on a flatting-block with a hammer (Plate 43, Fig. 3, *g*) and a setting-down tool (Plate 50, Fig. 2).

Wiring Curved Horizontal Edges

The edges of plates and salvers may be wired by a similar method. The wiring allowance is folded on a small stake or anvil, the edge of which is curved so that its radius fits, or is less than the radius of the work. The wire is inserted and closed, producing a flush wired edge.

If a raised wired edge is required, then the metal is set down on the face of the rim with a wide setting-down tool (Plate 50, Fig. 2), used with a hammer on a flatting-block.

The method illustrated for raised wired edges is one in which a steel grooving-block is used which forms the wire-groove in one operation (Plate 43, Fig. 4).

It is used with the small end of a Warrington-pattern hammer, which is ground to half an inch width with its corners well rounded off. The thickness of this end is also ground to the thickness of the wire used. The groove in the block (Plate 50, Fig. 3) is made with a small round file and, as the success of the method depends upon the nicety of adjustment of the hammer and groove, it is wise to test it repeatedly with small pieces of metal when the groove is being filed. The clearance should be just sufficient to allow the hammer to form the groove easily without binding. The groove depth should allow the finished wired edge to be raised or to be equally above and below the rim of the plate, as required.

The distance of the stops from the centre of the groove, which is the wiring allowance, is found by actually grooving a small piece of metal, inserting and closing a short length of wire, then annealing and opening it out flat. When all the adjustments are correct, the ends of the groove and all sharp corners are rounded off and polished. The stops should be an easy ' push ' fit in their holes.

In use, the wiring allowance is set out on the filed-up edge on the under side of the plate, and the forming of the groove commenced by striking light dead blows with the hammer on the line, forcing the metal down into the groove (Plate 43, Fig. 4, x). As this happens, the edge will rise up out of contact with the stops. The plate is rotated until the flat edge again makes contact with the stops and the grooving operation repeated round the plate. The stops are removed and the groove is then finished until it is of even depth. The wire is inserted and enclosed (Plate 43, Fig. 4, y). The ends are cut, tucked in and the edge finally closed (Plate 43, Fig. 4, z), cleaned off and flatted.

APPLIED WIRES AND MOULDINGS

The application of wires and mouldings to a free edge is an important constructional process which has been described in preceding chapters.

MOULDINGS

Drawn mouldings may be obtained from metal merchants, or drawn on a draw-bench if such equipment is available. Small astragal and reeded mouldings are generally the most useful and the ornate varieties of beaded mouldings should be avoided. Moulding may be made in short lengths on a hand-turning lathe. Rectangular or square wire is silver-soldered to a circle and tightly forced on to the edge of a piece of wide flat wood, which has been mounted on the lathe face-plate and turned circular. The metal circle is then trued and the moulding worked on its edge with hand turning tools, finishing with fine emery-cloth. It is then removed from the lathe, cut at the silver-soldered joint, annealed and

9

flatted.   A finished circle of moulding may also be jointed and turned by the same method to a pre-determined diameter.

CORDED WIRES

Simple decorative wires may be easily made by twisting, and many forms may readily be produced, the finished diameter depending upon the gauge of wires used.   It will be found that the simplest are the most successful and the following will form a basis for experiment :—

1. Double wire—loosely twisted.
2. Double wire—loosely twisted—hammered flat.
3. Double wire—tightly twisted.
4. Double wire—tightly twisted—hammered flat.
5. Triple wire—tightly twisted.
6. Triple wire—tightly twisted—hammered flat.

Effective combinations forming a wider band are easily possible.   For example, two double wires, twisted tightly in opposite directions, may be applied side by side or one double wire loosely twisted and flatted, may be applied between two straight square wires.

The length of the required corded wire is determined and 25 per cent. added to compensate for the contraction in twisting.   The wires are cut to this length and thoroughly annealed, pickled, scoured and dried.   The ends are placed in the side of a vice, the wires strained tightly to remove kinks and the free ends twisted for half an inch in pliers and inserted in the chuck of a hand-drill, which is then rotated slowly (Plate 44, Fig. 1). A reasonable tension is maintained during this operation, which may continue until a loose twist is formed.   It will usually be necessary to remove and anneal the wire very evenly at this stage if a tight twist is required, which may then be proceeded with.   The flat varieties are formed after this stage by lightly and evenly hammering on a polished flat stake with a convex planishing hammer.   The twisting of a corded wire will be perfectly even by this method if the annealing operations have been performed thoroughly and evenly.   If hardened patches are left they will not twist so tightly as the softer parts.

Nos. 18–22 S.W.G. are suitable gauges of wire for ordinary requirements.

Square wire may be twisted singly, but when applied it gives the optical illusion of a distorted or twisted edge, due to the shadows which are produced on the spiral faces.

PLAITED WIRE BANDS

These bands, the width of which varies according to the number of wires used, may occasionally be suitable. They are only effective if evenly worked and they are generally of very limited application.

1. Triple plait; in one, two or three parallel wires.
2. Quadruple plait; in one, two or three parallel wires.

No. 22 S.W.G. is the suitable gauge.

The wires are cut to length and evenly annealed and the ends inserted in a wood plaiting-cramp in the vice. The groups of wires are separated and arranged evenly, ready for commencing the plait (Plate 44, Fig. 2).

The method is exactly similar to that used in plaiting cord or string. Care must be taken to strain the group of wires held in each hand slightly outwards before the crossing of another group in order to keep the plait evenly tight. When about two inches have been plaited, the wires are moved back under the clamp. During the whole process it is necessary to prevent wires in the parallel groups from twisting in relation to each other.

CHAPTER XXVI

POLISHING AND COLOURING PROCESSES

Lustre—Removal of Blemishes—Final Surface Preparation—Polishing—Colouring—By Heat—Sulphur Solutions—Bronze Powders—Lacquers—Silver and Silver-plated Work.

THE property which allows the reflection of light from metallic surfaces is termed lustre. It does not follow that the metals which take the highest polish are the most lustrous. Copper alloys may be highly polished, but they are very readily acted upon by atmospheric gases and acids, which produce oxidation and corrosion. They are not, therefore, lustrous metals.

The property depends upon the retention of the polish, so that metals which take a high polish and are also immune from oxidizing and corroding agents which destroy the polish are lustrous. Gold and silver are high in a list of comparative metallic lustre.

In many instances the lustre of a metal is one of its most attractive features, but the maintaining of a high polish on work in copper, gilding-metal and brass by constant use of metal polish is undesirable. The wrought or hammered texture of the work soon disappears and as a result the surfaces become uninteresting. A suitable finish for work in these metals is that produced by the slow natural oxidation due to atmospheric gases, which gives a rich coloration or ' patina.'

In the case of silver and silver-plated work, the commercial ' black ' finish (so called because the polish is so high that shadows appear black) is not desirable. In use, the slightest scratch becomes at once obvious and the labour involved in maintaining the high polish is unwarrantable. The subdued lustre of antique silver is usually more appropriate.

As in decoration, restraint should be a characteristic of polishing.

Of the very many methods of executing these operations the simplest only are described, using hand equipment.

REMOVAL OF BLEMISHES

This operation has been dealt with in earlier chapters, and finished work should be finally inspected for tiny blemishes, scratches and file marks. They are removed with dead-smooth files and Water-of-Ayr stone, and the affected surface made good with ooo emery-paper, preferably glued on to thin pieces of wood. The care of the surfaces during working and skilful use of tools in the shaping operations will enormously minimize the labour involved at this stage.

Soft- and silver-soldered joints, folded and wired edges demand a good deal of attention. Excess solder, also films of solder which may have spread on to surfaces near a joint, should be carefully removed with safe-edged files and Water-of-Ayr slips, ground or filed to a suitable point. Folded and wired edges are cleaned off with files and fine emery-cloth, and the under edges filed true with safe-edged files and finished in the same way as joints. Bases other than those of sheet metal are ground flat on a rubbing-stone and are finished on a flat sheet of fine emery-cloth on a flatting-block.

Work should, if possible, be boiled-out in a weak sulphuric acid pickle to remove last traces of flux and other impurities. This should be followed by a boiling-out in strong soda water to remove acid which might other-wise reach and dry off in inaccessible parts. Finally, the work should be washed in hot soapy water.

Final Surface Preparation

It now becomes necessary to prepare the surface of the metal for the finishing operation, and this consists of the imparting of a soft satiny lustre by means of a very fine abrasive used with oil.

The work should be rubbed vigorously and evenly with crocus powder and thin machine oil or the finest pumice powder and raw linseed oil, on a small piece of rag, the latter being the cleaner in use. Inaccessible parts are scoured with the preparation used with a nail brush or similar stiff-bristled brush or on thin pointed pieces of wood.

When an even dull lustre is obtained, the work is again washed in hot soapy water and dried. If the previous suggestions concerning the polished faces of hammers and stakes have been observed, the surface preparation will present little difficulty.

Polishing

The lustre may now be easily raised by applications of a good-quality metal polish on a soft rag. The cheap domestic preparations should be carefully avoided. They sometimes contain gritty particles which scratch and ruin the previous surface preparation. Metal polishes suitable for silver should be specified. The work is finally rubbed with rouge on a dry chamois leather and washed in hot soapy water. The importance of this latter operation in maintaining lustre is not sufficiently realized. Frequent washing in hot soapy water will keep surfaces in excellent condition during use. Especially is this true of silver and silver-plated work.

Colouring

Work in copper alloys left in the finished condition will colour when handled or exposed to the air. In the case of copper and gilding-metal, a very pleasant patina is produced in time, which becomes a rich brown. In this condition it merely requires polishing by friction by occasional brushing with a fine brass wire scratch-brush and finishing with a soft rag. It is admittedly a long process, a polished job taking several months to colour, though quicker if the work can be stored in a room in which is a coke fire. It is well worth the time taken, as the patina being naturally produced is permanent under ordinary conditions. It may be artificially obtained, but is then more fugitive. The methods in common use are described :—

By Heat

If polished work is slowly and evenly rotated over a clean blowpipe flame it will assume a pleasant coloration, which is, however, extremely fugitive.

Sulphur Solutions

The work is first washed in strong soda water to remove all traces of grease and then immersed in a weak solution of ammonium sulphide by handling with brass tongs. (A clean vessel is filled with hot water and sufficient ammonium sulphide poured in to colour it a very pale yellow.) When the desired colour is obtained, the work is removed and washed in clean water and allowed to dry. It must not be handled or rubbed until dry. The surface can be lightly polished with a good wax furniture polish.

A similar finish may be obtained by dissolving a lump of potassium sulphide in hot water.   The work may be dabbed with a swab of cotton wool dipped in the solution, then washed and dried.

Bronze Powders

Pleasant brown finishes on copper may be obtained with proprietary bronze powders.   They are mixed with either strong ammonia or water, depending upon their type.   The work is painted with the compound, allowed nearly to dry and then brushed with brass scratch-brushes.

Lacquers

For work that is constantly handled, the foregoing processes are rarely satisfactory, the colour becoming patchy and generally fugitive.   Colourless lacquers are often recommended, but their use entirely spoils the texture of the work, giving it a shiny, treacly appearance.   The choice of finishes for such work, therefore, lies between a restrained lustre which must be maintained by light polishing and the friction-polished natural patina.

Silver and Silver-plated Work

There can be little doubt that the subdued lustre of old silver is one of the most attractive finishes for hammered metalwork.   It may be obtained on silver by the method described for copper alloys and, if desired, the work may be lightly coloured by a sulphur solution after the surface has been prepared.   The work is then finished to produce a very restrained lustre which can be maintained by washing in hot soapy water.   It should be noted that a sulphur solution for use on silver must always be used hot.

The same finishes may be produced on copper alloys after the electro-deposition of silver and is a very satisfactory solution to the finishing problem in those metals.   Work to be silver-plated must be very thoroughly prepared and special care taken in the removal of blemishes.   'They won't show when it is plated,' is a remark sometimes made by beginners, which could hardly be farther from the truth.

The work should be sent to a reliable firm whose integrity may be trusted and with clear instructions written on a tied-on label.   A cheap and scanty deposit of silver is unsatisfactory and the price paid should be such that will allow of a good deposit on the edges and corners, which are the vulnerable parts of plated work.

It is desirable to indicate the required treatment of the surfaces before plating, viz. :—'Hammered texture to be left,' or 'Smooth inside, hammered outside.'   Also the required finish of the plating should be stated, viz. :—' Plating left from the vat ' or ' Plating left from the scratch-brush ' or ' Plating polished.'

CHAPTER XXVII

DECORATION

Its Function—Suitability—Subordination—Restraint—Applications—Filed Ornament—Mouldings and Ornamental Wires—Surface Decoration.

THE aim of this volume is to present the constructional side of hammered metalwork as an aid in the gaining of manipulative skill in the processes. As decoration, however, plays such an important part in the design of examples of work in the craft, suggestions in that connection are considered very briefly.

Decoration in a constructional craft is that which adds interest or detracts from severity. It is not something separate and extra which is applied finally to make a job look attractive, but an integral part of its design which must be considered at the commencement. It is not, therefore, to be regarded as a separate process, though there are some processes of the craft which are wholly decorative, e.g. repoussé, chasing and enamelling.

The improvement in taste in recent years has been considerable and a tendency to simplicity has characterized design. Modern trend is that an object relies for its beauty on its good proportion, form, profile or surface finish rather than on large masses of applied ornament.

SUITABILITY

In the design of an example of craft work in wood of richly figured grain, it would be unwise to cover it with carved ornament. Such material lends itself to broad expanses of flat surface which display the beauty of the wood to the best advantage. In a similar way, the surfaces of hammered metalwork have a characteristic texture which should be preserved.

A finely and evenly planished surface has a charm of its own—not that planishing is essentially a decorative process. Nevertheless, a hand-worked metal surface which bears the legitimate facets made by the tool which was used finally to true it has a character which should remain unspoiled.

Further, a good deal of the attractiveness of such work is in the smoothness of its flat surfaces, or its even rotundity when handled. Large masses of raised ornament or narrow, deep fluting will detract from and in some cases completely mar such beauty.

It is wise, therefore, to rely for decoration on constructional features and the simple decorative treatment of handles, knobs, feet and mountings rather than on ornament which is applied to the detriment of the surfaces. Drawn mouldings of simple section are an actual part of the construction in that they reinforce a free edge and at the same time produce interesting bands of horizontal light and shade which give a sense of repose and stability to the work.

Subordination

If decorative treatment is on the lines suggested, it will be found that it is subordinate to the construction. This is very desirable, as work which is designed expressly to display large masses of decoration is frequently of very doubtful usefulness.

The design of an example of work should be on lines of utility and pleasing proportions, having, in addition, a feature of interest which may be a decorative treatment of part of the construction, or simple enrichment in sympathy with and supporting the construction—but never dominant.

If more than one part of a job is decoratively treated, the subordination of one to the other must again be considered. When, for instance, two mouldings are applied to a bowl or similar form, one should be smaller or more refined than the other, or else made to occupy a subsidiary position. Equal and therefore competitive features of interest produce a feeling of unrest and instability.

Restraint

Decoration is more effective when in contrast with plain, unrelieved or uninteresting areas, a fact which makes restraint in its use extremely important.

A practical example illustrates this point. A pair of silver bangles of native craftsmanship, one of which is shown in Plate 76, were required for reasons of their sentimental value to be converted to something of more general utility. In the light of modern design, their decoration, consisting of fluted bosses and wide bands of corded wires, is obtrusive and unrestrained, as it covers most of the surface.

The two bangles were therefore opened and seamed together, the resulting ring being incorporated in the mounting of a raised vase in silver.

The same decoration now assumes an entirely different character, as it is in more appropriate restraint, occupying a position of contrast with the larger areas of plain surface.

In many instances, the good shape or strong profile of a piece of work provides its own natural interest. In the case of a bowl or taller form having a curving profile, the area of its quickest curvature is usually the feature of interest. The application of a decorative wire or moulding to this position on the profile would be unnecessary. The supposed decoration would add nothing to the beauty of the work—rather would it detract from it, inasmuch as it tends to obscure the constructional feature of interest and also makes a break in a naturally strong profile.

Lack of restraint will, in addition, produce other totally incorrect applications of decoration which may even interfere with normal usage, e.g. the decorative modelling in high relief of the base of a plate or tray.

Many other injunctions and examples might be cited, but it is realized that decoration is not so much a matter requiring rules, as the acquisition of good taste, so that what is right and proper and of good design may be sensed rather than referred to classified regulations.

APPLICATIONS

Some of the simpler decorative operations are very briefly considered :—

FILED ORNAMENT

Pleasing decorative treatments of handles, knobs and feet may be given by the file in the shaping of these parts. One of the main requirements is that the file is used skilfully in the production of surfaces which should be of even and regular curvature and that all flat faces are truly flat and not rounded, ensuring that the corners formed by the intersection of the faces are sharp and precise.

MOULDINGS AND ORNAMENTAL WIRES

The application of mouldings and wires are, of course, constructional processes and have been described under previous headings. In the design of any work, it is important that lightness and refinement of mouldings are given full consideration, in order that edges may not be made to appear unduly heavy.

Of the two forms of applied mouldings the drawn varieties, astragal, half-round and reeded, are usually to be preferred to the more ornate rolled or pressed mouldings—beaded, egg-and-dart, etc.

The simpler forms of corded or twisted wires are also often suitable.

SURFACE DECORATION

In the designing of examples which form elementary exercises, to which the application of mouldings, wires or other similar decorative treatments would be unsuitable, simple surface ornament is sometimes appropriate. It should be of a form which does not interfere with the roundness or flatness of the work as a whole and its use must be restrained so that it is effective when in comparison with the larger areas of plain surface. Tooled or punch decoration may be used as a narrow band round a napkin-ring or on the top of a canister or as a cluster or grouped arrangement on a caddy-spoon handle. In general, its use should be avoided on all work which is not elementary in character.

The tools used are steel punches, which should depress a line from $\frac{1}{64}$ to $\frac{1}{32}$ inch in width, rather than a cut line which penetrates deeply into the metal. For this reason the points of the punches must not be sharpened to a cutting-edge, but should be evenly and smoothly rounded off and be of such a thickness that will depress a line of the necessary width.

It is desirable that a set of punches is designed and made, the impressions of which may be used as units in the building-up of patterns, in a similar way to the tooled decoration of book covers, except that for metal a 'solid' depression is not easily practicable and the ornament should therefore be restricted to lines. The line punches used as units may produce curves, circles and other 'closed' line-forms or the pattern may be built up entirely from straight lines.

Examples of typical punches (Plate 45, Figs. 1–7) and patterns produced by their combination are given (Plate 45, Fig. 8).

Experimental work in the arranging of a pattern is made easy if the tools are used on sheet lead or hardwood of close grain. It is also desirable that tools forming the basic units of a pattern should be made an even measurement—$\frac{1}{2}$ or $\frac{3}{8}$ inch, for example—to facilitate the setting-out on a metal surface. This operation is usually quite simple, consisting of a pencil centre line marked off in the correct interval for the basic impression and perhaps other parallel boundary lines which act as guides in the even and regular application of the remaining units (Plate 57).

The tool impressions are made in the previously annealed metal by light but decisive blows with a flat hammer. Flat work is supported on a smooth flatting-block and spherical surfaces on a suitably curved stake held in the vice. In flat work which is later bent and jointed to a cylindrical or conical form, e.g. a tooled band on a napkin-ring, the decoration is, of course, applied before bending and it becomes necessary to continue the decoration slightly beyond the ends so that they can be cut to ensure the correct repeat of the pattern over the joint. Care should be taken in jointing to use the minimum quantity of silver-solder. If an excess is used it will follow and fill up the line decoration when the work is at red heat. Should this happen, it will be necessary to re-strike the affected impressions after the joint has been cleaned off, the ring being supported on a suitable cylindrical stake.

Ring impressions or similar units which form groups or clusters may be very slightly raised with advantage as a second operation, by being struck lightly on the reverse side with a round punch, the metal being supported on a flat block of lead. This will probably distort the metal, and it must be flatted on the face side by very lightly re-striking the impressions with the original punches, the work resting on a flatting-block.

CHAPTER XXVIII

CONSTRUCTED AND IMPROVISED EQUIPMENT

Hardwood Equipment—Sinking-block—Hollowing-block—Saw-piercing Board—Mitre-block—Plaiting-cramp—Bending-former—Improvised Surface-plate and Grinding-block—Soldering-hearth—Metal Equipment—Petrol Vaporizer—Wiring-tools and Surface Decoration Punches—Scrapers—Grooving-tool—Grooving-block—Radius Stake—Joint-tool—Wire-cramp—Hammers—Heavy Equipment—Horse—Planishing Heads—Ball and Dome Stakes—Hatchet Stake—Stretching Stakes—Contracting Stakes—Cow-tongue Stakes—Cylindrical Stakes—Raising Stake—Vice-grips to Stakes—Flat Stake—Flatting-block—Snarling-irons—Made-up Equipment.

THE ability to produce or adapt one's own tools is especially desirable in hammered metalwork, though it is not essential. Much of the tool-equipment is not standardized and the results obtained with a constructed tool are often far superior to similar work executed with a bought article which is not designed for its specialized purpose. Occasionally a small operation presents itself for which no known tool is available and then something suitable must be invented or a modification of an existing tool made.

In addition, it is possible to improvise some really efficient substitutes for a quantity of the more expensive apparatus, from quite ordinary materials. The making of this equipment brings a sense of independence and adds enormously to the interest of the craft. Suggestions are given for this work, which is not of an advanced nature requiring a high degree of skill. It involves some of the elementary processes of woodwork and general metalwork, using the ordinary tools.

HARDWOOD EQUIPMENT

Equipment which requires the use of woodworking tools is dealt with first.

SINKING-BLOCK (Plate 46)

A 3-inch cube of almost any close-grained hardwood is suitable. On the end grain, the width of the rim of the work to be sunk is marked off from one edge and an arc of its circumference is set out on which are inserted two small nails which act as stops. A sinking-block will require frequent re-facing as the working corner soon becomes rounded.

HOLLOWING-BLOCK (Plate 46)

Sycamore, beech or birch are suitable hardwoods and a 5-inch cube is desirable. The depression is worked with a large outside-ground bent gouge and a mallet. It is tested with a segmental templet and finished with coarse glass-paper. (It is essential that the depression is worked on the end grain.)

SAW-PIERCING BOARD (Plate 46)

A short length of $3 \times \frac{3}{4}$ inch of almost any timber will serve. A $\frac{3}{4}$ inch hole is bored on the centre line about 3 inches from one end and saw cuts made into it, which produce a V-notch. Screw holes are bored at the other end for attachment to a bench.

MITRE-BLOCK (Plate 46)

A length of 2 inch square hardwood has a piece of wood $\frac{3}{4}$ inch wide and $\frac{3}{8}$ inch thick, screwed to one of its faces, parallel with the edge to form a rebate. The required mitre cuts are then made with a brass-back saw in an adjacent face. (The rebate may, of course, be worked in the solid.)

PLAITING-CRAMP (Plates 44 and 46)

The requirement is a simple cramp which will firmly grip a number of wires without damage. It is easily met in the provision of a piece of hardwood 6 inches long, $4\frac{1}{2}$ inches wide and 1 inch thick, curved on one side. Into this, at the centre, is halved a semi-elliptical piece 6 inches long, 2 inches wide and of similar thickness. Lengths of o B.A. or 2 B.A. screwed rod are inserted near the ends of the large piece, and a hardwood clamp 1 inch wide and $\frac{3}{8}$ inch thick is bored so that it fits over the rods. Pressure is applied to the clamp by wing-nuts and washers.

BENDING-FORMER (Plate 46)

The use of a lathe is required for making this valuable accessory for bending circles of wires and mouldings. It consists of a cylinder of hardwood on which are turned progressively smaller recesses. Shoulders for holding in a vice are sawn at the large end. A piece of old mangle-roller makes excellent material.

IMPROVISED SURFACE-PLATE AND GRINDING-BLOCK (Plate 47)

A large surface-plate is an expensive item which can be effectively improvised. A rectangular or square piece of $\frac{3}{8}$ inch mirror-glass or plate glass is obtained of any convenient size, 18 inches long and 12 inches wide, for example. A strong rebated oak frame is mortised and tenoned to fit the glass, glued up and cleaned off. The rebate should be about twice as deep as the glass thickness. The glass is fitted, its back painted with a white-lead paint and a wood fillet is planted round it and cleaned off flush with the frame. The glass is bedded by filling the recess very tightly with putty and screwing a $\frac{1}{2}$ inch wooden back securely to the frame. This completes the work for a serviceable and cheaply made surface-plate which is accurate for all ordinary purposes.

A very useful grinding-block may be made by taking the work a stage farther. An oak batten is prepared and recessed so that its edge fits accurately on to the face of the glass near its top end. Bolts are inserted in the frame and the batten ends are bored to receive them. A new sheet of strong, coarse emery-cloth is clamped under the batten, the free end being held down by one hand and the grinding executed with the other. If desired, a second batten may be fitted at the other end, thus leaving both hands free for the grinding operation. In addition to these two uses, the apparatus will serve as an effective flatting-block for annealed sheet metal, when a light mallet is used, provided that the glass has been thoroughly and evenly bedded.

SOLDERING-HEARTH (Plate 48)

Probably the most important piece of apparatus in a workshop for hammered metalwork is a soldering-hearth. It usually consists of an arrangement of fire-bricks on an iron tray, mounted on a bench with the foot-bellows screwed to the floor underneath it. A turn-table or revolving tray is almost a necessity, and there is little to choose between several methods of mounting it, provided that it remains truly horizontal during its rotation, and that it is sufficiently rigid to support the weight of the work being soldered without the possibility of movement other than rotation on its vertical axis.

Sometimes a self-contained or portable hearth is an advantage in a school workshop which is used for other crafts. The general details of such a hearth are given without particular measurements, which may vary considerably. A strong hardwood frame is jointed, having horizontal rails, which carry two shelves and a top. The foot-blower is mounted on the right of the lower shelf and the upper one carries the lower bearing or pivot of the turn-table. A sheet-iron tray of about 3 inches depth is made and screwed to the top (which should be not less than 1 foot 6 inches square) with a sheet of hard asbestos between the tray and the wooden top. The front of the tray is open, and an extension of its base is rounded over the wooden top to protect it from the blowpipe flame. The hearth is built into the tray, with $1\frac{1}{2}$ inch thick fire-brick slabs, set in fire-clay. These slabs may be obtained in suitable sizes from a good builder's merchant. The turn-table top is made from $\frac{1}{8}$ or $\frac{3}{32}$ inch mild-steel plate and is fitted with four struts made from two lengths of $\frac{3}{4}$ inch wide and $\frac{1}{8}$ inch thick mild steel. The spindle of $\frac{1}{2}$ inch mild-steel rod has shoulders turned at either end, the upper end being riveted or screwed to the struts, whilst the other end forms the lower bearing. A 1 inch hole is left in the assembly of the fire-brick slabs, and also bored through the tray and top. Bearing-plates are fitted to the top and upper shelf respectively. When used as an open hearth, loose fire-bricks are arranged round the sides as required, the turn-table being removed.

The turn-table, in use, should be faced with fire-brick or asbestos and an additional course of loose fire-bricks can be used if higher screening is required for tall work. The blowpipe is hung at the right-hand side and should be connected up with light rubber tubing. (If convenient the apparatus may be made from angle-iron.)

An air-reservoir can be improvised and fitted alongside the bellows for the purpose of delivering a steady blast to the blowpipe. It may consist of an air-tight oil-drum fitted with a $\frac{1}{2}$ inch pipe to the blowpipe and another similar pipe from the bellows which should be provided with a simple form of non-return valve at its point of attachment to the reservoir.

METAL EQUIPMENT

Elementary tool-making with very simple equipment is considered, and a section is also included for which the use of a metal-turning lathe and forge is necessary.

PETROL VAPORIZER (Plate 49)

Suggestions for a petrol vaporizer are given in a sketch which should be regarded as diagrammatic. The arrangement shown consists of an

10

inner tank of sheet metal, preferably brass, fitted with a flanged lid. The size may be about 12 × 8 × 5 inches. The sides are drilled to accommodate lengths of tube which pass through the tank, and are soft-soldered in place. Their number is unimportant—the more the better. A large number of long wicks are tied on to the tubes, the free ends resting on the bottom of the tank. To the lid is soldered a ½ inch gas outlet and also a screw filler-cap with a tubular extension. The lid is finally soft-soldered on and the whole of the joints carefully checked for leaks. The outer tank consists of a hot-water jacket of similar construction, considerably larger than the petrol tank. It is fitted with a vented filler-cap in its lid and a drain-cock in its base. The inner tank is supported on metal strips, clear of the base, and the gas lead and petrol filler must pass through holes in the outer lid, which is finally soft-soldered. The vaporizer may be mounted on low wall-brackets outside the workshop, the gas lead being taken through the wall to the blowpipe, which should be used as near to the vaporizer as possible. This arrangement complies with fire regulations restricting quantities of petrol inside a workshop. When used, the inner tank is half filled with petrol and the jacket is filled with boiling water. The vaporizer will feed a ½ inch blowpipe and, when finished with, the drain-cock is opened.

The jacket may be fed directly from an existing hot-water system, in which case a larger drain-cock would be required and it should then be fitted with a waste-pipe.

A simpler workable arrangement consists of the inner tank only, which is warmed by pouring a pail of boiling water over it. In this case thin rods could take the place of tubes for the wick-support.

WIRING-TOOLS AND SURFACE DECORATION PUNCHES

Punches and similar small tools for special purposes are so frequently required, that practice in this simple form of tool-making should be considered essential. Generally these tools consist of a 4 inch length of ½, ⅜, 5⁄16 or ¼ inch square, octagonal or round tool-steel, tapered, shaped, polished, hardened and tempered. Sketches of a tracer (Plate 50, Fig. 1), and setting-down tool (Plate 50, Fig. 2), used in edge-wiring are included as examples.

The tapering operation may be performed by two methods, drawing-down at red heat, or by filing cold. The former is the quicker method, and should be used wherever possible.

Drawing-down a Flat Taper

The end of a length of tool-steel is heated to a full red in a forge fire, or with a blowpipe on a soldering-hearth, and is hammered on the beak of an anvil or on a flat stake, to spread it.   It is then rotated 90 degrees, and struck lightly on the adjacent face, to restrict the side spreading to the required dimension and to force the point forwards.   These operations are repeated until the dimensions of the point are $\frac{1}{16}$ inch in excess of those required for the breadth and thickness.

Drawing-down a Circular Taper

This process is carried out in three stages, by drawing-down a square taper and then working it octagonal by hammering the corners, and finally circular, slowly rotating the octagonal taper whilst it is being lightly hammered at red heat.

Upsetting

When the end of a punch or other tool, e.g. a snarling-iron (Plate 24), is required to be thick or wide, it becomes necessary to upset the end before shaping.   This consists of thickening the end previously, to provide the extra metal.   A short length of tool-steel is held in tongs and its end heated, and the metal held vertically with the hot end on the anvil or stake face. The upper cold end is then struck heavily with a bench hammer so that the hot end is thickened.   The work should be trued before each re-heating to restore its correct alignment.

Heat Treatment

Tool-steel should not be worked below a full red heat, neither should yellow be exceeded.   In the event of overheating or ' burning,' the whole of the affected metal must be removed before proceeding.   When a shaping operation is concluded, the work must be heated to a full red and cooled very slowly so that it is thoroughly annealed.

Cutting Tool-steel

Tool-steel may be cut with a hacksaw liberally oiled, or it may be nicked round with a file, placed in a vice with the filed nick just projecting and broken off.

Shaping

The shaping of the point is worked with files and finished with emery-cloth.   If an emery-wheel is available, it should be used for the removal of waste metal, finally finishing with files and emery-cloth.

Filing a Taper

Occasionally it may be more convenient to execute the whole of the shaping by filing.   Filed circular tapers must pass through three stages, square, octagonal and finally circular.

Ring punches should have the depression in the end made at red heat with a round-nosed punch, the waste metal then being removed with coarse files and a taper produced which finishes at the depression, leaving the edge of the circle the correct thickness.

Hardening and Tempering

The final operation in the making of tool-steel punches is the hardening of the point and then reducing the degree of hardness to produce toughness, which is called tempering.   The two processes may be executed in one operation, but better results are usually obtained when they are performed separately and it is, therefore, described in this way.   The finished taper is smeared with soap to prevent scaling and is heated very slowly and evenly to a dull red heat and then quenched vertically in a pail of lukewarm water to which a handful of salt has been added.   It should be tested with an old file, and if the hardening is correct it cannot be filed.   The taper is now very thoroughly polished with a long strip of emery-cloth, and the punch held at its extremity in tongs.   A small, hard blowpipe flame is applied to the centre of the shank of the punch, which is slowly rotated.   As the heat travels from the centre to the point by conduction, a band of colours appear on the polished steel moving towards the point. These colours indicate a degree of heat which is sufficient to reduce the hardness from ' dead hard ' to the annealed state, but they are only useful in indicating the temper of tool-steel which has been previously hardened. The colours appear on the silvery white of the polished steel in the following order, pale yellow, straw, dark straw, yellow-brown, brown, brown-purple, light purple, dark purple, dark blue, blue, light blue, blue-green, blue-grey, after which the metal becomes red hot and is, of course, annealed.   If the centre of the punch is heated slowly, these colours spread out into a wide band, which moves slowly.   They will, in turn, pass out at the point of the punch, which should be quenched in oil when it is brown. It will then be substantially hardened, but sufficiently tough to withstand the shocks of normal use.   A point so tempered may be filed with difficulty.

SCRAPERS

A scraper for cleaning off soft-solder is made from $\frac{3}{16}$ or $\frac{1}{4}$ inch square tool-steel or from an old square file.   One end is spread to $\frac{3}{8}$ inch and squared up with a file.   A bevel of about 70 degrees is filed on the squared end (similar to a setting-down tool) and a right-angled bend made $\frac{3}{8}$ inch from the end, the bevelled edge being on the outside. The other end is drawn down to a square tang for fitting to a file handle.   The tool is hardened and tempered to a light yellow, the edge being finished on an oilstone.

Two scrapers should be made, one having a flat working edge (for use in corners) and another of very slight curvature (for use on flat surfaces).

A scraper for removing blemishes from a metal surface consists of the rounding (by grinding) of the end of each face of an old triangular file, producing a triangular point with sharp corners which is curved in its length.   The tool should remain dead hard, the faces being finally smoothed on an oilstone (Plate 7, Fig. 5).

GROOVING-TOOL (Plate 50, Fig. 4)

A grooving-tool is made by filing the groove $\frac{3}{16}$ or $\frac{1}{8}$ inch wide with a small round file in the squared end of a length of $\frac{3}{4} \times \frac{1}{2}$ inch tool-steel. The corners are rounded off and the end hardened and tempered to a yellow-brown.   A wider tool is made if the end of the material is previously upset and flatted to $\frac{1}{2}$ inch thickness.

GROOVING-BLOCK (Plate 50, Fig. 3)

This tool is made from 1 inch square tool-steel.

RADIUS STAKE FOR PLANISHING SMALL SINKINGS (Plate 50, Fig. 5)

The correct double curvature is filed on the end of a length of tool-steel, which may be from $1\frac{1}{2} \times \frac{3}{4}$ inch to $\frac{3}{4} \times \frac{1}{2}$ inch, depending upon the size of the sinking to be planished.   The working face is hardened and tempered to a yellow-brown and then thoroughly polished.

JOINT-TOOL (Plate 50, Fig. 6)

This tool consists of a short length of $\frac{3}{4} \times \frac{3}{8}$ inch or $\frac{5}{8} \times \frac{5}{16}$ inch tool-steel having a $\frac{1}{4}$ or $\frac{3}{16}$ inch hole drilled on its centre line near one end.   The

hole is filed to a square internal angle and into it is drilled and tapped a
2 B.A. or 4 B.A. screw.   One face of the end of the tool containing the
hole is polished and finally hardened.   It is not tempered and the success
of the tool depends upon the squareness of the hole with the face of the
metal, especially the filed internal 90 degree angle.

WIRE-CRAMP (Plate 50, Fig. 7)

A wire-cramp may be made after the style of outside calipers, but is
more readily adapted from spring-calipers.   The ends of this tool must be
heated and re-bent, so that 1 inch of metal on each leg is straight, the two
becoming a straight line when the tool is opened about 1½ inches.   Two
pieces of channel-section mild or tool-steel are constructed by brazing or
silver-soldering.   They should be about 1 inch long and one face of
each is fitted with a 4 B.A. wing-screw.   A blind countersunk hole is
drilled in each leg of the calipers so that the wing-screw will enter it and
secure the channel-blocks in position when the wire to be silver-soldered is
gripped between the opposite face and the caliper leg.   Other arrangements for gripping the wire may be easily devised, such as small screw-
clamps on each caliper-leg, the only requirement being that the wire is
held rigidly and that a small amount of spring-pressure may be applied to
the ends of the wire.

HAMMERS

The desirability of making or adapting hammers which are suited
exactly to the work is obvious when the lack of standardization and high
cost of the bought article is considered.   A useful working set of hammers
consists of eight, all of which may be adapted from the No. 1 or No. 2
Warrington pattern head.   The No. 1 is suitable for school use, and is a
lighter edition of the No. 2.   The shape and curvature of each in the
No. 2 size is shown in plan and elevation, and a scale is included.   A good-
quality solid cast-steel hammer should be obtained for conversion, and that
manufactured by Messrs. Brades, of Sheffield, is recommended.

The hammer head is placed across an open vice and the shaft struck
through the eye with a hammer and drift.   The first four in the series—
flat and convex planishing, stretching and hollowing—may be converted
hard, i.e. without annealing.   The use of an emery-wheel is necessary and
each face is slowly rotated against it until the required even curvature is
obtained.   The flat planishing hammer (Plate 51, Fig. 1) simply has its

sharp corner removed and the convex planishing hammer (Plate 51, Fig. 2) is almost imperceptibly rounded and its corner removed. The stretching and hollowing hammers (Plate 51, Figs. 3 and 4) each have an increasing degree of curvature. The rough faces are then cleaned up on a fast-cutting oilstone, and great care is needed in obtaining a truly spherical curve at the centre of the faces. They are then polished on coarse and fine emery-cloth, their shafts re-fitted and securely wedged.

The remaining four hammers (Plate 51, Figs. 5 to 8) are shaped by elementary forging operations. The heads are first slowly annealed, and then drawn down to size at full red heat. The raising hammer (Plate 51, Fig. 6) must be spread with fullers to obtain the necessary width. White heat must be carefully avoided in each case. They should be annealed, the waste metal removed, and the faces worked to shape on an emery-wheel. The final cleaning up is done with files and emery-cloth. The faces are smeared with soap, to prevent scaling, and the heads heated very slowly to a dull red heat and hardened by being quenched vertically in lukewarm water. The last operation consists of softening the eye, after the faces have been re-polished. This may be easily done by heating the eye very evenly with a blowpipe flame and quenching the head in oil, the instant the bright face becomes a very pale yellow colour. It is necessary that the face of the hammer be left very hard and the pale yellow tempering colour of the face must be watched for carefully during this last operation. The shafts are then re-fitted and wedged.

The finishing sizes of the No. 1 heads will, of course, be proportionately smaller.

The curvatures of the faces are of far greater importance than the actual sizes, special care being required in the cases of the convex planishing and stretching hammers.

Heavy Equipment

Under this heading is given particulars of the larger stakes, for the making of some of which a metal-turning lathe is necessary, and the use of other machine-tools desirable.

Horse (Plate 52)

The end of a length of 1 inch square tool-steel is drawn down from 1 inch to $\frac{5}{8}$ inch thick, the thinning being progressive and the side spreading restricted to $1\frac{1}{4}$ inches on the upper face of the bar. A $\frac{5}{8}$ inch square, slightly tapered hole is punched hot, at the thin end, on the centre line of the face of the bar and the internal tapered faces of the hole cleaned up with files. The bar is then bent hot to a right-angle, at about 5 inches from the hole. The other arm forms a vice-grip, or the waste may be left, its face cleaned off and polished and used as a flat stake for planishing folded work.

PLANISHING HEADS (Plate 52)

A set may be turned from 2 or $2\frac{1}{4}$ inch round mild-steel bar, the radius of the profiles of the set becoming progressively smaller. A recess may be turned for the lug, which is then filed square and tapered to fit the hole in the horse. If shaping or milling machines are available, a square parallel lug may be formed first. The profile is then turned in a four-jaw chuck, cleaned off, polished and the lug tapered with files to fit the horse.

Planishing heads may be improvised by mounting solid oven-door and other steel or iron knobs in the end of a 1 inch square mild-steel bar, either vertically or horizontally.

BALL AND DOME STAKES (Plate 52)

Stakes of this class of any desired profile may be turned from 3 inch round mild steel, or smaller square steel may be previously upset to provide the necessary metal and then turned.

HATCHET STAKE (Plate 52)

A 10-inch length of $2\frac{1}{2} \times \frac{1}{2}$ or $2 \times \frac{3}{8}$ inch mild steel, with 6 inches of one edge filed or machined to a 30-degree bevel, makes a good hatchet stake. The thickness of the working edge should be from $\frac{3}{32}$ to $\frac{1}{16}$ inch.

STRETCHING STAKES (Plate 52)

Short lengths of $1\frac{1}{2} \times \frac{3}{4}$ mild or tool-steel with their edges rounded to various radii may be made for many internal stretching operations.

CONTRACTING STAKES (Plate 52)

Two examples are given of contracting stakes made from $1\frac{1}{2} \times \frac{3}{4}$ and 1-inch square mild or tool-steel bar. These stakes usually require to be made specially for a particular curvature.

Cow-tongue Stakes (Plate 52)

$1\frac{1}{4}$ inch square steel bar is suitable for the forging of the heavier varieties of this type of stake. As in the previous case, they are usually forged to suit a particular class of work.

Cylindrical Stakes (Plate 52)

Short lengths of mild-steel machine shafting of various diameters under 4 inches may be used without any alteration other than polishing. It is desirable, however, to face the ends for use as canister stakes or planishing stakes for bases. If they can be turned from square bar, the centre makes a convenient vice-grip. Taper-turned stakes of this class, and also one of about 3 inch diameter turned slightly convex in its length for the planishing of cylindrical work, are extremely useful.

Raising Stake (Plate 52)

Cylindrical stakes may be used for raising, though they are more suitable if their working face is of flatter curvature. They may be turned from $2\frac{1}{2}$ or 2 inch round or square steel bar, the working face being turned from a second offset centre and having about a $1\frac{1}{2}$ inch radius. The end should be ' backed-off ' to 70 degrees and the tip very slightly rounded.

Vice-grips to Stakes

Wherever possible, $\frac{5}{16}$ or $\frac{1}{4}$ inch round studs should be inserted in the sides of constructed stakes to prevent them gradually slipping through the jaws of the vice when in use. The studs should project not more than $\frac{3}{16}$ inch and should usually be arranged so that one of them projects under the vice-jaws and one over them, when the stake is in its normal working position.

Flat Stake

A domestic flat-iron inverted in a vice makes a good flat stake for small work. The horizontal round handle may be removed and a spacing piece of iron or mild steel screwed or riveted between the uprights of the handle to form a vice-grip.

FLATTING-BLOCK

The essentials of this tool are its weight and flat surface, free from blemishes. It should be at least 1 inch thick, and of as large a size as possible, and may be either mild steel or cast iron. The surface may be machined in a shaper, planer or lathe and then polished.

SNARLING-IRONS (Plate 24, Fig. 2)

The end of a length of $\frac{1}{2}$ inch square tool-steel bar is upset and the head forged to the required shape and cleaned off. Two right-angle bends, about 12 or 15 inches apart, complete the work. The head should be from $1\frac{1}{2}$ to 2 inches above the horizontal part.

MADE-UP EQUIPMENT

In cases where no facilities exist for heavy metalworking, it should be realized that the work may be made up quite reasonably at general machine-shops, garages and the like, from simple dimensioned or full-sized drawings. Any stake shape may be cast at a foundry in malleable cast iron from a wood pattern, which must be supplied with the order.

The foregoing constructed tools should not be regarded as a complete essential equipment. They are merely included as examples of the type of tool which can be made to suit general and particular requirements.

The local blacksmith will be an expert tool-maker and can be a friend-in-need on very many occasions. The chief thing necessary is to know exactly the size and shape of a stake required for a particular class of work, so that adequate directions may be given with the order.

A visit to a local waste-metal merchant is usually well worth while and an iron and steel scrap-heap will often yield readily convertible material which can be purchased quite cheaply. Parts of discarded machinery can sometimes be put to useful service. A small cone pulley, for example, makes an excellent bending-former for circles of wires and mouldings, and part of an old circular-saw table may be used as a good flatting-block.

It is not claimed that such improvised equipment is as efficient as the specialized article it may replace. It is, however, extremely useful where cost is an important consideration, as it then permits of much work being successfully undertaken which would be impossible without its aid.

If the requirements of each process of the craft are thoroughly understood, it becomes an easy matter to see at a glance the type of improvisation which will repay the labour involved in the conversion.

CHAPTER XXIX

EXAMPLES OF PRACTICAL WORK

A COURSE of work is included for one purpose only—to apply the methods which have been considered in the preceding chapters. The examples should be regarded as suggestions for practice in the fundamentals rather than as an inflexible course which must be slavishly copied.

Imitation is only of value in the early stages of work in a craft when the most important consideration is the obtaining of experience of the processes and tool operations together with a knowledge of the properties of the material.

When reasonable manipulative skill is acquired, the aim should be to become creative rather than imitative. Inspiration derived from a study of old and contemporary work and a realization of the essentials of modern design will, as practice is obtained, develop individuality.

No opportunity should be lost for contact with craftsmen, and an hour's practical demonstration will provide more stimulus than can be expected from a prolonged study of a text-book.

In this chapter brief working notes are included for each example, together with a scale drawing and photograph.

The essential processes and tool operations have been classified, explained and illustrated in preceding chapters. The working notes, therefore, suggest an order of procedure, with a reference to the illustration of each operation which is further explained in the text. In the early examples these references are given in detail and in later ones only the fresh or specialized operations are so referred, those previously dealt with being omitted.

In some cases the sketches referred to illustrate the particular operation concerned. In cases where they do not, they indicate that a similar process or arrangement is applicable.

Commencing and intermediate sizes are omitted. If dimensioned directions for the making of every part of each example were given in detail, a very valuable part of the training would be lost—that of making a working drawing and from it estimating the commencing sizes and determining the various allowances.

The necessary procedure is therefore to make a full-sized drawing from the reduced scale drawing by transferring measurements from it with dividers to the scale provided, and then to use this full-sized drawing as a basis for estimating commencing sizes and preparing patterns and also to provide a check on the final dimensions of each part.

It is realized that this preliminary work requires more time and also that results (in the early stages only) may not be quite so accurate, due to the need for experiment, as if detailed measurements were given. No apology is offered, however, as it has been conclusively proved that confidence and independence are more readily acquired when the whole of the work is undertaken at the commencement than when the examples are constructed from prepared directions. The aim is, therefore, to present the practical work in such a way that these essential qualities in a craftsman are developed in the shortest time and that the production of the examples is a secondary consideration, being merely a means to that end.

It is suggested that the early examples are made in copper, this metal being easily worked and responsive to the shaping processes. Some of the examples lend themselves to execution in brass. Gilding-metal should be the material for advanced work in which all joints are silver-soldered. Experience should be gained in the working of silver and every opportunity taken for its use, especially when precision in the use of the tools has been acquired.

The metal gauges suggested err on the side of heaviness. In the early stages it will be found that thick metal is easier to shape than thin. It is more rigid during a shaping operation, also stretching due to over-hammering is less apparent than it would be in a light gauge.

Work in silver should naturally be lighter than in the base metals. Refinement, which is the characteristic of silver, is seriously impaired if work in that metal feels heavy and cumbrous when handled.

The practical work included in this chapter will be found to contain the basic constructional processes and tool operations of the craft. Some of the later examples do not come under the heading of elementary work and it is not to be expected that they can all be undertaken by beginners. They have, however, been executed successfully either by students at the Board of Education Vacation Courses for teachers or by students at a non-specialist Training College for teachers during a one-year metalwork course.

EXAMPLE No. 1. SMALL TRAY (Plates 53 and 65).

1. Estimate the diameter of the required flat disc (or blank) and add $\frac{1}{16}$ inch waste allowance (Plate 6, Fig. 2).

2. Cut a square from No. 20 S.W.G. sheet metal.

3. Anneal and prepare the surfaces (Plate 7).

4. Set out the blank circle with wing-compasses (Plate 8, Fig. 1).

5. Cut the circle (Plate 9, Fig. 2), and file its edge smooth.

6. Set out a pencil circle corresponding to the internal limit of the surface-decoration.

7. Mark off points on the circle which indicate the intervals of the surface-decoration.

8. Apply the surface decoration, using a ring-punch and flat hammer, the metal being supported on a flatting-block.

9. Make an inside templet for the hollowing, in tinplate or thin card (Plate 30, Fig. 1).

10. Work the hollowing with a small sinking hammer in a hollowing-block (Plate 16, Fig. 1).

11. Flat the base (Plate 18, Fig. 4), true up the hollowing (Plate 32, Fig. 2).

12. Grind the rim flat (Plate 33, Fig. 6), and test the truth of the circle in plan (Plate 30, Fig. 2).

13. Prepare the surface and polish.

EXAMPLE No. 2. PIN BOWL (Plates 53 and 65)

1. Cut and prepare estimated blank circle, plus $\frac{1}{8}$ inch waste allowance, from No. 18 or 19 S.W.G. sheet metal (Plate 6, Fig. 1).

2. Make inside templet.

3. Work hollowing with a hollowing hammer of large radius.

4. Anneal and planish bowl concentrically, using a dome stake of suitable size and a flat planishing hammer (Plate 28, Fig. 6).

5. Estimate and cut length of $\frac{1}{4} \times \frac{1}{8}$ inch metal to form bowl-mounting (or base-ring).

6. Anneal and flat.

7. Set out a line with wing-compasses on one face which is $\frac{1}{16}$ inch from the edge (Plate 8, Fig. 2).

8. Bevel the edge with a file to the line—i.e. file the edge $\frac{1}{16}$ inch 'out of square.'

9. With the bevelled edge inwards, bend the strip to a circle (Plate 13, Fig. 3), the diameter of which equals the upper and smaller diameter of the finished mounting.

10. Cut (Plate 10, Fig. 4), and square the ends with a file.

11. Silver-solder the butt joint (Plate 37, Fig. 2).

12. Pickle mounting and clean off the joint.

13. Stretch lower square edge of mounting, producing conical form of correct dimensions (Plate 19, Fig. 4).

14. Flat and true up (Plate 31, Figs. 4 and 5).

15. Indicate the centre of bowl on outside.

16. Set out circle on outside of bowl, equal to the top diameter of the mounting.

17. Fit mounting to bowl by filing down the high places on the bevelled upper edge of mounting with half-round file.

18. Soft-solder mounting to bowl (Plate 36, Fig. 2).

19. Clean off joint with safe-edged smooth file filled with chalk.

20. Grind base of mounting flat (Plate 33, Fig. 6).

21. Apply circle and remove waste from bowl rim.

22. Flat the rim and round the edge with smooth files, finishing the edge only, with emery-cloth.

23. Prepare surfaces and polish.

EXAMPLE No. 3. NAPKIN RING (Plates 53 and 65)

1. Estimate, set out, cut and prepare the commencing rectangle in No. 20 S.W.G. sheet metal (Plate 8, Fig. 3).

2. Set out the folding-lines which will form the corners, stepping off the intervals with wing-compasses to ensure similarity.

3. With the folding lines upwards, fold to hexagonal form on corner of square bar by hand pressure (Plate 15, Fig. 1).

4. Fit the joint (Plate 33, Fig. 2), and silver-solder (Plate 37, Fig. 1).

5. Clean off joint, removing all excess silver-solder.

6. Mallet the faces flat on face of square bar, working up the corners as sharply as possible.

7. True up the hexagon and planish the faces, using a convex planishing hammer (Plate 28, Fig. 2).

8. Re-true the hexagon and grind edges flat.

9. Finish and polish.

EXAMPLE No. 4. TUMBLER STAND (Plates 53 and 65)

1. Add $\frac{1}{4}$ inch to the finished diameter when determining the commencing circle, to form a waste margin.

2. Cut and prepare the circle in No. 18 S.W.G. sheet metal.

3. Planish radially, using a convex planishing hammer of large radius (as in Plate 28, Fig. 1).

4. Anneal, pickle and flat.

5. Set out finishing circle, thus indicating the waste margin.

6. Estimate and cut length of $\frac{3}{16}$ inch astragal or suitable drawn moulding.

7. Anneal and bend to shape on bending-former (Plate 13, Fig. 3).

8. Cut and square ends in joint-tool (Plate 33, Fig. 3).

9. Silver-solder joint in wire-cramp (Plate 38, Fig. 2).

10. Clean off joint, finishing with Water-of-Ayr stone.

11. Flat and true up circle of moulding.

12. Pin the moulding to base and soft-solder with panels of soft-solder applied on the waste margin (Plate 36, Fig. 1).

13. Clean off internal edge of joint, if necessary.

14. Remove waste margin (Plate 9, Fig. 5).

15. Draw-file the edge, finish and polish.

EXAMPLE No. 5. PIERCED RING (Plates 54 and 66)

1. Estimate rectangle length by bending a piece of wire to the plan drawing.

2. Cut and prepare rectangle in No. 18 S.W.G. sheet metal.

3. Set out pencil centre-line, outline, and finally the pierced ornament. (This may be executed on paper and secured to metal by a strong adhesive.)

4. Drill $\frac{1}{16}$ inch entry-holes and cut piercing (Plate 11, Fig. 1).

5. Clean off edges with suitable Swiss files.

6. Indent the lines indicating the overlap of centre cross-bands with small chisel or tracer and chasing hammer.

7. Cut and clean off the outline.

8. Bend to circle, silver-solder and clean off joint.

9. Planish very lightly on cylindrical stake (Plate 28, Fig. 3).

10. Press to elliptic form and true up with mallet on suitable stakes.

11. Clean off and polish.

EXAMPLE No. 6. HEPTAGONAL TRAY (Plates 54 and 66)

1. Cut and prepare blank circle having $\frac{1}{8}$ inch waste allowance, in No. 20 S.W.G. sheet metal.

2. Set out circle forming the sinking-line (avoiding centre-mark on base).

3. Work sinking on hardwood block (Plate 18).

4. Planish base radially, on flat stake (Plate 28, Fig. 1).

5. Planish sinking concentrically (Plate 29, Fig. 1).

6. Planish rim by grouping (Plate 28, Fig. 1).

7. Set out heptagon on rim.

8. Set out centre lines and guide circles in pencil for surface decoration.

9. Apply surface decoration.

10. Cut heptagonal outline and slightly round off corners.

11. Flat the surfaces and polish.

EXAMPLE No. 7. SMALL VASE (Plates 54 and 66)

1. Develop truncated cone pattern from elevation drawing (Plate 5, Fig. 3).

2. Cut and prepare No. 18 or 19 S.W.G. sheet metal, to pattern.

3. Bend to conical form with mallet on bick-iron (Plate 13, Fig. 4).

4. Fit, silver-solder (Plate 37, Fig. 4), and clean off joint.

5. Planish the cone (Plate 28, Fig. 4), then anneal.

6. Draw circle on paper, equal to diameter of centre-line of surface decoration.

7. Mark intervals of surface decoration on circle.

8. Cut out the paper circle and slip remainder of paper over the cone and transfer interval marks to the cone with a hard pencil.

9. Set out pencil height-line on cone at the centre of surface decoration by resting pencil on block of wood of suitable height (as in Plate 30, Fig. 4, *a*).

10. Apply surface decoration (with work on bick-iron).

11. Stretch top of cone internally, with collet hammer on rounded corner of steel bar (Plate 19, Fig. 2).

12. Contract base of cone on specially shaped contracting-stake (Plate 20, Fig. 1).

13. Grind top and base edges flat, and round over the top edge with smooth files and emery-cloth.

11

14. Cut No. 20 S.W.G. base circle.

15. Soft-solder the base to body with small panels of soft-solder arranged on the inside of the base (as in Plate 36, Fig. 3).

16. File the edge of the base circle to continue the profile of the contraction.

17. Prepare the surfaces and polish.

EXAMPLE No. 8.   HOLLOWED TRAY (Plates 54 and 66).

1. Estimate and cut No. 18 or 19 S.W.G. circle, having $\frac{1}{8}$ inch waste allowance (Plate 6, Fig. 2).

2. Proceed as for Example No. 1, paragraphs 9, 10 and 11.

3. Planish the base radially.

4. Planish the hollowing concentrically, on suitable radius or cow-tongue stake (Plate 29, Figs. 1 and 2).

5. Estimate, cut, bend, fit and silver-solder ends of circle of $\frac{3}{16}$ inch astragal moulding and clean off joint.

6. Flat and true up circle.

7. Apply ' tinning ' of soft-solder to under face of moulding (sufficient should be applied to make the face fairly convex) (Plate 35, Fig. 1).

8. Soft-solder circle of moulding to tray (Plate 35, Fig. 2).

9. Clean off joint with wedge-pointed Water-of-Ayr stone.

10. Apply internal height-line (Plate 8, Fig. 8), and remove waste (Plate 9, Fig. 6).

11. Clean off top edge, prepare surfaces and polish the tray.

EXAMPLE No. 9.   HEXAGONAL PLATE (Plates 55 and 67).

1. Estimate, cut and prepare circle in No. 20 S.W.G. sheet metal.

2. Continue as in example No. 6, paragraphs 1 to 6.

3. Set out hexagon on rim.

4. Estimate and cut length of $\frac{1}{8}$ inch half-round wire.

5. Anneal, pickle and flat.

6. Bend to hexagon with rounded corners, using short length of round iron bar vertically in vice as a bending former for each corner.

7. Flat and true up hexagon, using hexagon drawn on cartridge paper as templet.

8. Cut ends, fit, silver-solder with hard-running silver-solder and clean off joint, which should occur at the centre of a flat side rather than on a rounded corner.

9. Pin wire to plate and silver-solder joint (with easy-running silver-solder), the silver-solder being applied to waste margin (Plate 37, Fig. 5).

10. Remove waste and clean off edge and also the internal angle of the joint.

11. Flat and prepare the surfaces and polish.

EXAMPLE No. 10. RAISED TRAY (Plates 55 and 67)

1. Estimate, cut and prepare circle plus ⅛ inch waste allowance, in No. 20 S.W.G. sheet metal.

2. Set out the base circle on the reverse side of disc.

3. Raise to shape and height, using a small raising hammer and raising stake (Plate 23, Figs. 1, 2 and 3), allowing side to finish concave.

4. Planish base on under side, using a convex planishing hammer and a canister or bottom stake (Plate 28, Fig. 5).

5. Planish upper part of the side internally with a convex planishing hammer and a cylindrical stake (as in Plate 29, Fig. 5).

6. Remove the waste edge, clean off and true up horizontal edge (Plate 32, Fig. 3).

7. Estimate and twist tightly three lengths of No. 18 S.W.G. annealed wire (Plate 44, Fig. 1), and hammer flat.

8. Bend to circle, cut, fit and silver-solder ends in wire cramp and clean off the joint.

9. Pin triple corded wire circle to edge of tray and lightly squeeze with smooth-nosed pliers so that the wire conforms to the sloping side of the tray.

10. Soft-solder or silver-solder the wire to the tray and clean off the joint with a brass wire scratch-brush.

EXAMPLE No. 11. CADDY SPOON (Plates 55 and 67)

1. Estimate a commencing circle for the bowl hollowing and also find the length of the handle in the flat.

2. Make a templet in thin card or tinplate and cut the blank in No. 18 S.W.G. sheet metal.

3. Work the hollowing, allowing the handle to assume a natural angle in relation to the bowl.

4. Planish the hollowing and clean off all edges.

5. Flat the handle.

6. Estimate and make a templet for the handle overlay.

7. Cut No. 18 S.W.G. sheet metal to the templet and prepare its surfaces.

8. Set out and apply the clustered punch decoration.

9. Clean off and finish the edges.

10. Pin the overlay to the handle and silver-solder (Plate 38, Fig. 1).

11. Clean off the joint with pointed Water-of-Ayr stone.

12. Bend the handle to shape on a cylindrical stake by hand pressure, finally truing it up with a mallet.

13. Finish the surfaces and polish.

EXAMPLE No. 12. HOLLOWED BOWL (Plates 55 and 67)

1. Add $\frac{3}{8}$ inch to the estimated diameter of the blank.

2. Cut and prepare circle in No. 20 S.W.G. sheet metal.

3. Make inside templet and work the hollowing.

4. Planish bowl on suitable dome or ball stakes.

5. Bend and silver-solder circle of $\frac{1}{4} \times \frac{1}{8}$ inch to form cylindrical mounting.

6. Lightly planish mounting and fit it to bowl.

7. Silver-solder mounting to bowl (Plate 38, Fig. 4), and clean off joint.

8. Grind base flat and set out two internal height-lines, the lower one equal to the height of the finished bowl, and the upper one, this first height, plus the width of the thrown-out horizontal edge.

9. Stretch the thrown-out edge (Plate 42, Fig. 3, a and b).

10. Tightly twist two No. 18 S.W.G. wires and silver-solder the ends in wire cramp to form a double corded wire circle which is $\frac{1}{8}$ inch less in diameter than the maximum outside diameter of the bowl under the thrown-out edge.

11. Set out guide circle on thrown-out horizontal edge, of such a width as will expose half the corded wire when viewed in plan.

12. Remove the waste, flat and clean off edge.

13. Invert the bowl on flatting-block and press the corded wire circle into position with a piece of wood, stretching it until it lies closely and evenly in contact with the thrown-out edge.

14. Pin the corded wire to bowl and soft-solder by direct application of the soft-solder from the stick (Plate 36, Fig. 4).

15. Clean off the corded wire with a brass scratch-brush.

16. Finish the surfaces and finally polish.

EXAMPLE No. 13. TANKARD (PINT) (Plates 56 and 68)

1. Develop the required truncated cone, the side of which should be a straight line joining the base and top.

2. Set out and cut from No. 18 S.W.G. sheet metal.

3. Bend, fit, silver-solder and clean off seam.

4. Stretch to shape and planish on a cylindrical-type stake (Plate 52) having a profile, the curvature of which is slightly 'quicker' than the required profile of the tankard body. If this stake is not available, the profile may be planished on a cylindrical stake and finished straight (Plate 28, Fig. 3).

5. Grind top and base edges flat.

6. Estimate length of handle in the flat, and cut from $\frac{1}{2} \times \frac{1}{4}$ inch metal.

7. File handle to shape and finish with smooth files and emery-cloth. (Alternatively, the handle may be forged at red heat from a shorter length by drawing down the ends, rounding and finishing with files and emery-cloth.)

8. File the rounding on each end of handle. (A quadrant in front-elevation and a semicircle in side-elevation.)

9. With the rounded ends inwards, bend handle to shape on length of $\frac{3}{4}$ inch round bar in vice (Plate 13, Fig. 2).

10. Tie handle to body, rouge vertical joint in body and silver-solder handle to body (Plate 39, Fig. 2).

11. Re-planish upper and lower extremities of body very lightly to harden the metal.

12. Cut, bend, silver-solder and clean off ring of $\frac{1}{8} \times \frac{1}{16}$ or $\frac{1}{16}$ inch square wire, so that it finishes $\frac{1}{8}$ inch slack in base of body.

13. Planish to a tight push fit in body.

14. Silver-solder wire ring to base circle, cut from No. 20 S.W.G. sheet metal with $\frac{1}{4}$ inch waste margin (Plate 37, Fig. 6).

15. Remove waste margin, clean off edge and fit completed base into body.

16. Soft-solder base to body (as in Plate 36, Fig. 3), and grind base flat.

17. Prepare the surfaces and polish.

EXAMPLE No. 14. SEAMED VASE (Plates 56 and 68)

1. Estimate and develop the necessary truncated cone, the side of which should be a continuation of the lower straight part of the body (Plate 6, Fig. 6). $\frac{3}{16}$ inch should be added to the height.

2. Set out and cut from No. 18 S.W.G. sheet metal.

3. Bend, fit, silver-solder and clean off seam.

4. Stretch to shape on funnel stake (Plate 19, Fig. 1).

5. Planish on cylindrical and funnel stakes.

6. Grind base edge flat.

7. Round over top edge.

8. Estimate, cut, bend, silver-solder and clean off ring of $\frac{1}{4} \times \frac{1}{8}$ inch metal, the internal diameter of which is equal to the external diameter of the base of the body.

9. Stretch ring to conical shape, true up and grind top edge flat.

10. Cut a circle in No. 18 S.W.G. sheet metal, the diameter of which equals the outer diameter of the top of the conical ring.

11. Silver-solder the circle to the conical ring and round over the upper corner, finishing with smooth files and fine emery-cloth.

12. Estimate, cut, bend, silver-solder and clean off ring of $\frac{3}{16}$ inch astragal moulding, the internal diameter of which is $\frac{1}{32}$ inch less than the external diameter of the base of the body, to ensure a tight fit.

13. Fit ring of moulding to body. Remove and silver-solder ring to base, rouging the previous joints in base. Fit base to body and soft-solder (Plate 36, Fig. 3).

14. Clean off joints and grind base flat.

15. Set out internal height-line, remove waste, true up, clean off and round top edge.

16. Prepare surfaces and polish.

EXAMPLE No. 15. CIRCULAR DISH (Plates 56 and 68)

1. Estimate and cut blank in No. 19 S.W.G. metal, allowing $\frac{1}{4}$ inch waste margin.

2. Hollow to shape (Plate 16, Fig. 2), and planish. True up very accurately.

3. Estimate and bend to development curve length of $\frac{1}{8}$ inch half-round wire for rim (Plate 6, Fig. 9).

4. Set out rim circle on outside of bowl, thus indicating waste margin.

5. Bend, fit and pin wire to bowl and silver-solder (Plate 39, Fig. 3).

6. Remove waste margin and clean off cut edge, with a slight inside rounding.

7. Flat bowl edge and true up accurately.

8. Estimate and cut rectangle in No. 18 S.W.G. metal to form bowl mounting.

9. Silver-solder length of $\frac{1}{8}$ inch half-round wire to it, in the flat (Plate, 37 Fig. 5), using hard-running silver-solder.

10. Bend to circle, silver-solder (Plate 37, Fig. 1) and clean off seam.

11. Internally stretch to shape and $\frac{1}{16}$ inch in excess of finished diameter (Plate 19, Fig. 2).

12. Using a false centre (Plate 8, Fig. 5) set out the final circle and remove waste, finishing the edge vertical with smooth files.

13. Estimate and cut length of $\frac{1}{4} \times \frac{1}{8}$ inch metal to form base-ring.

14. File quadrant on one edge and clean off.

15. Bend to circle, silver-solder with hard-running silver-solder and clean off joint.

16. Silver-solder mounting to base-ring (arranging as in Plate 35, Fig. 4).

17. Fit top edge of mounting to bowl and set out a location circle on bowl. Check horizontal level of bowl when in position on mounting.

18. Silver-solder mounting to bowl (Plate 38, Fig. 4), rouging joint between mounting and base-ring.

19. Prepare surfaces and polish.

EXAMPLE No. 16. TEA-POT STAND (Plates 57 and 69).

1. Experiment to find the necessary wiring allowance, using No. 19 S.W.G. sheet metal and No. 16 S.W.G. wire (Plate 6, Fig. 10).

2. Find radius of the required circle with addition for wiring allowance.

3. Cut and prepare No. 19 S.W.G. sheet metal.

4. Inscribe and cut hexagon.

5. Flat, and set out wiring allowance.

6. Set out and apply surface-decoration.

7. Remove small waste V-notches at the corners of wiring allowance. (Their shape and size should be determined by experiment on similar waste metal.)

8. Fold wiring allowance down to 90 degrees, using a mallet and small steel block with slightly rounded corner and true up very accurately.

9. Bend length of No. 16 S.W.G. hard-drawn wire to a hexagon which accurately fits inside the folded wiring allowance (Plate 13, Fig. 1).

10. Cut and fit overlapping ends of wire.

11. Fit and enclose the wire by malleting the wiring allowance over it.

12. With a pencil, mark off the width of the wired edge on the face side.

13. Set down the wired edge on the face side, working to the pencil line, using a light hammer and setting-down tool (Plate 43, Fig. 2, Stage G to H).

14. True up the internal corners, also the completed wired edge.

15. Soft-solder wired edge on reverse side by direct application, avoiding an excess of soft-solder.

16. Cut and mitre the sides of the base frame in $\frac{1}{4} \times \frac{1}{8}$ inch metal (Plate 10, Fig. 6), and file the lower recesses in each.

17. Assemble and silver-solder the corner joints and clean off the completed hexagonal base.

18. Soft-solder the base to the top and clean off.

19. Prepare the surfaces and polish. (This example should be worked hard, without annealing.)

EXAMPLE No. 17. ASH BOWL (Plates 57 and 69)

1. Estimate and cut in No. 19 or 20 S.W.G. sheet metal the required blank, assuming the top edge to be vertical instead of contracted.

2. Hollow to shape, with vertical edge.

3. Planish and true up accurately.

4. Contract the top edge on small mushroom stake (as in Plate 20, Fig. 4).

5. Cut four blanks for feet, in No. 20 S.W.G. sheet metal.

6. Hollow to shape in lead block or in doming-block (Plate 16, Fig. 3).

7. Grind edges flat and file a small nick in edges to provide air-vent during jointing.

8. Tin the edges.

9. Set out pencil circle on bowl which will contain the centres of the feet.

10. Set out location circles on bowl for feet with wing-compasses.

11. Soft-solder feet to bowl, with the filed nicks to the inside (Plate 35, Fig. 6).

12. Grind and round over the top edge.

13. Clean off joints, prepare surface and polish.

EXAMPLE No. 18. CANISTER (Plate 57)

1. Calculate rectangle size for the body.
2. Cut from No. 19 S.W.G. sheet metal.
3. Bend to cylinder.
4. Fit, silver-solder and clean off seam (Plate 37, Fig. 3).
5. True up (Plate 30, Figs. 3 and 5) and planish the body parallel, with the exception of the upper half-inch, which should be very slightly contracted.
6. Grind top and base edges flat.
7. Cut base circle (with $\frac{1}{2}$ inch waste allowance).
8. Cut wiring slots in base and bend up stops (Plate 38, Fig. 6).
9. Estimate length of $\frac{3}{16}$ inch astragal moulding.
10. Remove one fillet and clean off cut edge.
11. Bend to circle which is $\frac{1}{16}$ inch too small for fitting on body and silver-solder and clean off butt joint.
12. Set out moulding height-line on body (Plate 8, Fig. 7).
13. True up and fit circle of moulding and force it down the slightly contracted top of body, until it registers very accurately with the height-line.
14. Pin moulding to body and tie the base in position.
15. Rouge the vertical joint in body.
16. Silver-solder moulding and base in one operation (Plate 39, Fig. 4 and Plate 38, Fig. 6).
17. Remove waste margin from base and clean off the joints.
18. Cut, bend and silver-solder No. 19 S.W.G. sheet metal to form vertical rim of lid, the diameter of which should be $\frac{1}{16}$ inch too small for body.
19. Lightly planish to a good easy fit on body.
20. Internally stretch the quadrant on the top edge, on a square bar with a rounded corner, using a collet-hammer (Plate 19, Fig. 2, a and b).
21. Cut top of lid in No. 19 S.W.G. sheet metal.
22. Set out and apply surface decoration. Hollow and lightly planish.
23. Fit lid to rim, tie and silver-solder.
24. Clean off joint and slightly round off the edge.
25. Grind base of lid rim flat.
26. Finish the surfaces and polish.

EXAMPLE No. 19. HOLLOWED DISH (Plates 57 and 69)

1. Cut, prepare and hollow bowl in No. 19 S.W.G. sheet metal.
2. Planish bowl, finishing rim on cylindrical stake (Plate 29, Fig. 5).

3. Remove one fillet from length of $\frac{3}{16}$ inch astragal moulding and clean off edge.

4. Silver-solder to No. 18 S.W.G. strip in the flat.

5. Cut to length, bend to circle and silver-solder butt joint.

6. Clean off joint and contract top with mallet.

7. Proceed as in Example No. 2, Paragraphs 15–21.

8. True up horizontal edge (Plate 32, Fig. 3) and finish smooth.

9. Execute surface preparation and polish.

EXAMPLE No. 20. SMALL TANKARD (HALF-PINT) (Plates 58 and 70)

This is an alternative tankard to Example No. 13.

The construction is similar except that the upper bend of the handle is made on $\frac{3}{4}$ inch round bar and the lower one on $\frac{5}{8}$ inch, also the profile is straight.

EXAMPLE No. 21. BEAKER (Plate 58)

1. Estimate and develop contracted cone (Plate 6, Fig. 7).

2. Cut, bend and silver-solder in No. 18 S.W.G. metal.

3. Prepare contracting-stake (Plate 52) from $1\frac{1}{2} \times \frac{3}{4}$ inch mild-steel or tool-steel, with the correct profile.

4. Contract body to shape (Plate 20, Fig. 3). Anneal and planish.

5. Cut, silver-solder and clean off ring of $\frac{3}{16}$ inch astragal moulding a tight push fit on lower end of body.

6. Cut a circle in No. 20 S.W.G. metal an accurate and easy fit inside ring of moulding.

7. Cut, bend, silver-solder and bevel ring of $\frac{3}{16} \times \frac{1}{8}$ inch metal. Round off upper corner.

8. Silver-solder moulding, base-circle and base-ring together, in one operation.

9. Grind base of body flat and insert in completed mounting.

10. Soft-solder body to mounting (Plate 36, Fig. 3).

11. Set out internal height-line. Cut rim and grind flat.

12. Clean off and polish.

EXAMPLE No. 22. WIRED PLATE (Plates 58 and 70)

1. Estimate and cut circle in No. 20 S.W.G. metal, allowing $\frac{1}{16}$ inch in addition to the necessary wiring allowance.

2. Execute the sinking.

3. Planish the sinking internally, using a flat stake and well-fitting large sinking-hammer (Plate 29, Fig. 3).

4. Planish the rim by grouping.

5. Planish the base radially, finishing on a stake having a curvature of large radius to produce the slight convexity of the base.

6. Remove waste on edge of rim and clean off. Set out wiring allowance on reverse side of rim.

7. Prepare grooving-block (Plate 50, Fig. 3), and execute the wiring (Plate 43, Fig. 4), using No. 12 S.W.G. wire.

8. Finish surfaces of plate and polish.

EXAMPLE No. 23.   COVERED PLATE (Plates 58 and 70)

If a glass liner is used it will, to some extent, determine the size of the sinking of the plate. The dimensions of the working drawing may therefore require to be proportionately altered unless a liner is obtained of a similar diameter and depth.

1. Estimate and cut circle for plate in No. 19 or 20 S.W.G. metal, allowing a $\frac{1}{4}$ inch waste margin.

2. Execute sinking and planish so that the liner, if used, is a good easy fit. (The sinking-depth should be $\frac{1}{8}$ inch in excess of the overall height of the liner.)

3. Planish and carefully flat the plate rim, paying special attention to the flatting of the corner of the sinking.

4. Cut, bend and silver-solder the ends of circle of $\frac{3}{16}$ inch astragal moulding to form rim moulding.

5. True up and silver-solder rim moulding to plate.

6. Remove waste, clean off and finish plate.

7. Estimate and cut blank for the cover in No. 18 or 19 S.W.G. metal.

8. Hollow to shape and planish so that its rim is an easy fit into the plate sinking.

9. Grind rim flat.

10. Remove one fillet from length of $\frac{3}{16}$ inch astragal moulding, cleaning off the cut edge.

11. Bend and silver-solder to a circle $\frac{1}{16}$ inch less in diameter than rim of hollow cover.

12. With the cover on the face of a flatting-block, press the circle of moulding into position, using a length of No. 14 or 16 S.W.G. wire (held

round the cover and in contact with the flatting-block) as a distance-stop, to ensure that the lower edge of the moulding is parallel with the edge of the cover.

13. Pin the moulding to cover and silver-solder (Plate 39, Fig. 3).

14. Make the bent wire handle (Plate 14), and silver-solder to cover (Plate 39, Fig. 2), pinning and rouging the previously made joint between moulding and cover.

15. Clean off and polish completed cover.

EXAMPLE NO. 24.   INKSTAND (Plates 59 and 71)

1. Prepare pattern for stretched cone with allowances.

2. Cut, bend, silver-solder and clean off in No. 18 S.W.G. sheet metal.

3. Internally stretch to shape (Plate 19, Fig. 3).

4. Anneal and planish.

5. Insert false wood centre and set out top circle, also base circle plus a $\frac{3}{32}$ inch allowance for turned-down rim, or fillet (Plate 8, Fig. 5).

6. Remove waste and contract turned-down rim (Plate 20, Fig. 2).

7. True up both edges and grind flat.

8. Twist length of double corded wire in No. 20 S.W.G. wire.

9. Bend and silver-solder wire circle $\frac{1}{16}$ inch less in diameter than base.

10. Cut length of $\frac{1}{4} \times \frac{1}{8}$ inch metal for base ring, round the edge and clean off.

11. Bend to circle, silver-solder and clean off joint.

12. Load base rim of body with soft-solder (Plate 35, Fig. 3).

13. Press corded wire circle over turned-down rim.

14. Weight or tie body to base-ring and flush soft-soldered joints (Plate 35, Fig. 4).   (Alternatively these joints may be silver-soldered.)

15. Prepare circle for top of body in No. 20 S.W.G. sheet metal, with $\frac{1}{8}$ inch allowance on radius for folded edge.

16. Turn down edge to right angle so that top of body is an accurate internal fit (Plate 20, Fig. 2).

17. True up and grind edge parallel and flat.

18. Cut hole in top for inkwell with piercing-saw.

19. Remove one fillet from length of $\frac{3}{16}$ inch astragal moulding.

20. Bend and silver-solder to circle to fit inkwell top.

21. Silver-solder circle to inkstand top.

22. Fit top to body and turn folded edge over so that the stretched top edge of body is enclosed in the completed folded edge.

(The inkstand top may be silver-soldered directly to the body as an alternative to the folded edge, in which case it must be jointed before the base is applied, if soft-solder is used on the base.)

23. Prepare, cut and hollow circle for lid in No. 19 or 20 S.W.G. sheet metal.

24. Planish and contract (Plate 20, Fig. 4) to an easy fit over the applied circle of moulding on inkstand top.

25. Grind edge flat.

26. File up or hand-turn ball for knob and soft-solder to lid (Plate 35, Fig. 5).

27. Prepare surfaces and polish.

EXAMPLE No. 25.   RAISED BOWL (Plates 59 and 71)

1. Cut and prepare the blank circle (with an allowance for the folded edge) in No. 20 S.W.G. sheet metal.

2. Raise bowl, using wedge raising-mallet, commencing on a mushroom stake and finishing on a ball stake (Plate 22). (The folded edge allowance becomes an addition to the vertical height.)

3. Planish on suitable stakes.

4. Estimate and cut circle for raised bowl-mounting in No. 18 or 19 S.W.G. sheet metal.

5. Raise to steep-sided conical form, using raising-hammer and raising-stake (Plate 23, Figs. 1–4).

6. Remove flat centre with piercing-saw.

7. Shape cone by concave contraction (Plate 20, Fig. 3), and clean off edges.

8. Prepare and make base-ring in $\frac{1}{8}$ inch square wire.

9. Silver-solder butt joint with hard-running silver-solder.

10. Fit mounting to bowl and also to base-ring.

11. Tie the base-ring and mounting to bowl and silver-solder both joints (by direct application) at the one firing (Plate 38, Fig. 4).

12. Grind base flat and clean off silver-soldered joints.

13. Set out internal height-lines, remove waste and fold top edge (Plate 42, Fig. 3).

14. Clean off folded edge.

15. Prepare and polish surfaces.

EXAMPLE No. 26.   CIGARETTE BOX (Plates 59 and 71)

This example makes use of an unconventional hinge which departs somewhat from normal practice. The lid is flanged by $\frac{3}{16}$ inch astragal moulding, and the assembly of the hinge is such that its proportions are similar to the moulding, so that the hinge appears to be a part of the moulded edge of the lid. One fillet of the astragal is removed and the remainder is jointed to three sides of the lid, the metal thickness of which replaces the removed fillet. On the hinge side of the lid the chenier, or hinge-tube, continues as the round centre member of the astragal moulding and the hinge-bearer becomes the lower fillet. The appearance of the hinge side of the box is, therefore, similar to the front except for the joints in the chenier.

1. Set out and cut folded box in No. 18 S.W.G. sheet metal (Plate 6, Fig. 4).

2. Bevel the inside vertical edges of the box sides.

3. Fold the sides (Plate 15, Fig. 4) and silver-solder the corner joints. (Alternatively the sides may be folded from one strip and silver-soldered at one corner and then to a base. Another method is to fold adjacent faces from one piece, producing two right-angles of metal which are silver-soldered together and then to the base.)

4. Clean off joints and true up accurately.

5. Round off external corners and finish them with fine emery-cloth.

6. Remove one fillet from $\frac{3}{16}$ inch astragal moulding and clean off the cut edge and flat.

7. Bend accurately to fit round front and sides of box, cutting and squaring the ends so that they project $\frac{1}{16}$ inch beyond the back.

8. Cut, hollow and planish box top in No. 18 S.W.G. sheet metal.

9. Cut and finish edges and slightly round the corners so that lid dimensions exactly equal those of the remaining fillet on moulding.

10. Pin and silver-solder moulding to lid, carefully checking the distance apart of the ends.

11. Draw down length of No. 12 S.W.G. tube in circular drawplate (Plate 33, Fig. 4) until its diameter equals that of the round centre member of the astragal moulding, then cut to the box length, plus $\frac{1}{2}$ inch.

12. Using a circular needle file or small round Swiss file, cut semi-circular grooves in the projecting ends of the moulding already soldered to lid.

13. Test the tube in these grooves, and if necessary deepen them so

that the tube lies close up to the remaining side of the box when the lid is placed in position. (The back edge of the top should be exactly over the centre line of the tube.)

14. Pin tube to lid and silver-solder, keeping true alignment of tube. (The lid should, at this stage, be an easy fit on the box.)

15. Divide tube on lid into five equal parts and remove the second and fourth with a flat file, being careful not to remove metal from the lid, especially at its edge. (A piece of paper pasted inside will also protect it from file scratches.) The ends of the gaps so formed must be very carefully squared with a safe-edged file.

16. A length of $\frac{1}{16}$ inch square wire is thinned on one face with a file or by hammering, to equal the thickness of the lower fillet of the astragal moulding.

17. Place lid and wire in position, mark location and silver-solder the wire to the box as a hinge-bearer.

18. Cut and fit two lengths of tube to the gaps in lid.

19. Mark locations and silver-solder these to hinge-bearer. (The tube ends should be rouged during this operation.)

20. Draw well-fitting wire for hinge-pin and cut $\frac{5}{8}$ inch shorter than box side.

21. Finish and polish box and lid.

22. Insert hinge-pin. Check height of hinge-bearer.

23. Plug holes in ends of tube with well-fitting wire which has been previously tinned. Flush the tinning with small flame.

24. Clean off wire projections at hinge corners and round off corners of tubes.

25. If desired the box may be lined with thick saw-cut veneer, the base being fitted and then the sides mitred in with a small application of very hot, thin glue.

EXAMPLE No. 27. SWEETS DISH (Plates 60 and 72)

1. Hollow and planish bowl (allowing $\frac{1}{4}$ inch waste margin) in No. 20 S.W.G. sheet metal.

2. Set out octagon on bowl rim.

3. Mitre (Plate 10, Fig. 6), pin and silver-solder moulding and remove waste. (The moulding may be $\frac{1}{8}$ or $\frac{3}{16}$ inch astragal or reeded or any suitable drawn section.)

4. Raise or seam bowl-mounting in No. 18 S.W.G. sheet metal.

5. Contract to shape and planish, allowing $\frac{1}{8}$ inch waste margin at the base.

6. Cut base to octagon, clean off both edges and flat.

7. Mitre and silver-solder octagonal base with hard-running silver-solder, using $\frac{1}{4} \times \frac{1}{8}$ inch metal. File bevel.

8. Fit bowl-mounting to base-octagon.

9. Silver-solder mounting to base-octagon.

10. Flat bowl rim, avoiding damage to moulding.

11. Fit mounting to bowl, tie and check the horizontal level.

12. Silver-solder mounting to bowl.

13. Clean off and polish.

The moulding may be silver-soldered to the bowl rim as a final operation if desired, giving an opportunity of truing the horizontal level of the bowl rim relative to the base (Plate 32, Fig. 3).

EXAMPLE No. 28. TEA CADDY (Plates 60 and 72)

1. Cut and raise body in No. 20 S.W.G. sheet metal, using raising hammer (Plate 23).

2. Planish base on canister stake (Plate 28, Fig. 5).

3. Planish side on cow-tongue stake (Plate 29, Fig. 2).

4. Wire top edge (Plate 43, Fig. 3) with No. 16 S.W.G. wire, clean off (Plate 33, Fig. 5) and polish.

5. Shape lid by mallet raising or hollowing.

6. Planish lid and stretch thrown-out edge, allowing $\frac{1}{8}$ inch waste margin.

7. Cut edge of lid so that half of wired edge, in plan, is exposed when lid is in position.

8. Bend, silver-solder and planish $\frac{1}{4} \times \frac{1}{16}$ inch ring to a good fit in body.

9. Silver-solder ring to lid.

10. File up hexagonal knob from round ebonite rod.

11. Drill tapping hole and tap 4 B.A. internal thread (Plate 11, Fig. 5).

12. Drill clearance hole in lid. Clean off and polish.

13. Make or fit 4 B.A. screw and fix knob.

EXAMPLE No. 29. TRINKET BOX (Plates 60 and 72)

1. Assemble body of box in No. 19 S.W.G. sheet metal by silver-soldering butt or mitred joints, using hard-running silver-solder.

2. Silver-solder body on base.

3. Commence the parting of lid from body at one corner (to provide air-vent) with brass-back saw (Plate 11, Fig. 3).

4. Silver-solder top to lid, applying silver-solder to small waste margin.

5. Complete the parting of lid from body.

6. Grind lid and body edges flat.

7. Build up and silver-solder stop-hinge (Plate 41).

8. Assemble liner in No. 21 S.W.G. sheet metal by silver-soldering mitred joints.

9. Cut and silver-solder thumb-grip in filed recess in lid.

10. Fit liner and soft-solder. (The soft-solder is fed to the inside base-corner and the heat applied near the top, drawing the soft-solder vertically up the joint by capillary attraction.)

11. Clean off all joints and slightly round over the sharp corners.

12. Grind the surfaces with Water-of-Ayr stone and polish.

EXAMPLE No. 30.   CANDLESTICK (Plates 61 and 73)

The individual components of this candlestick of old-time pattern present little difficulty, the exercise being mainly one of fitting and assembly.

1. Hollow and planish the bowl in No. 20 S.W.G. sheet metal.

2. Twist and silver-solder the double corded wire (No. 18 S.W.G.), under a thrown-out edge which exposes half of the corded wire thickness in plan (as in Example No. 12).

3. Silver-solder and planish a ring in No. 19 S.W.G. strip, $\frac{3}{8}$ inch wide, which is a good fit on the base of the candles used.

4. Cut, hollow and planish loose grease-pan and contract its turned-up edge.

5. Remove its centre and silver-solder ring of strip to it. Clean off joint and round over the upper edge.

6. Seam, stretch and planish the nozzle so that the grease-pan is a tight push fit into its upper end.

7. Remove centre of bowl with piercing-saw and silver-solder nozzle.

8. Cut, bend and finish handle and silver-solder to bowl, a recess being filed in the thrown-out bowl edge to receive the top of the handle.

9. File or hand-turn ball feet and silver-solder to base.

10. Fit and soft-solder the small base in the nozzle.

11. Finish the joints and surfaces and polish.

12. Replace and check the final tight fit of the grease-pan.

EXAMPLE No. 31.   OCTAGONAL BOX (Plates 61 and 73)

This box is of similar construction to Example No. 29 except that the body and liner are folded from one strip (Plate 15, Fig. 1), instead of being assembled in separate pieces.

EXAMPLE No. 32.   POWDER BOWL (Plates 61 and 73)

1. Raise bowl in No. 19 or 20 S.W.G. sheet metal and planish.

2. Assemble and silver-solder bowl-mounting to bowl (ring of $\frac{3}{16}$ inch astragal moulding and rounded base-ring of $\frac{1}{4} \times \frac{1}{8}$ inch metal).

3. Silver-solder applied $\frac{1}{8}$ inch half-round wire to bowl rim and grind flat.

4. Finish surfaces and polish.

5. Hollow and planish lid and cut to correct diameter.

6. Silver-solder ring of $\frac{1}{4} \times \frac{1}{16}$ inch strip to lid, an easy push fit in body.

7. Bend and cut rings for handle in $\frac{1}{8}$ inch round wire (Plate 10, Fig. 5).

8. Insert one ring in the other, close joints and silver-solder each joint with hard-running silver-solder and clean off.

9. Arrange rings in correct position (with joints together) between two small pieces of soft wood.

10. Squeeze the pieces of wood in vice, remove rings and silver-solder them together in the same relative position.

11. File small flat on base of completed ring handle and silver-solder to lid (Plate 38, Fig. 3).

12. Finish and polish lid.

EXAMPLE No. 33.   RAISED VASE (Plates 61 and 73)

A tall raised form with a contracted neck may be regarded as being among the more advanced examples of raised work. A commencement is made on a raising-stake with a raising-hammer and a straight-sided raised form produced (a). When the base-angle is reached, the base is worked to its correct diameter and trued. Succeeding courses commence progressively higher up the profile, producing curved sides which become parallel at the height of the shoulder of the vase and continue parallel to the extremity of the metal (b). The contraction at the shoulder is commenced on a suitable mushroom or dome stake and proceeds as long as the stake will enter the neck of the contracted form (*c*). (Continuing beyond this stage would imprison the head of the stake behind the neck.) It now becomes necessary to make a cow-tongue type of stake from 1 inch round iron or steel. The bar is forged oval and then bent so that its external curve equals the final profile of the vase neck. The contraction of the neck is then completed on this stake, using a small collet-hammer. The vase may be filled with an equal mixture of hot pitch and plaster-of-paris for the final planishing. The raising of tall forms and the experimental work involved in the making and adapting of suitable stakes is one of the most interesting aspects of the craft.

EXAMPLE No. 34. SUGAR BOWL (Plates 62 and 74)

1. Make elevation drawing ($\frac{1}{16}$ inch narrower than the required finished size).
2. Develop pattern (Plate 5, Fig. 2), and cut in No. 19 S.W.G. sheet metal.
3. Mark folding-lines and fold to shape (Plate 15, Fig. 1).
4. Fit joint, silver-solder and clean off.
5. Lightly planish faces (avoiding final concavity) and true up flat.
6. Grind lower edge flat and set out height-line.
7. True top and grind flat.
8. Fit and silver-solder base in No. 19 S.W.G. sheet metal (Plate 38, Fig. 5).
9. Prepare surfaces and polish.

EXAMPLE No. 35. CREAM JUG (Plates 63 and 74)

1. Proceed as for example No. 34, Paragraphs 1–8.
2. Bend, planish and true up spout. The corner of the spout should be rounded at the top, running to a sharp fold at the base. It is important that the sides of the spout, in plan, should exactly continue the two faces of the hexagonal body when the completed top edge is finally ground flat.
3. Mark body from spout, remove waste (less the metal-thickness of spout), fit the joint, silver-solder (Plate 39, Fig. 1), and clean off.
4. Set out and cut handle outline in $\frac{3}{4} \times \frac{1}{8}$ inch strip metal.
5. File edge bevels and folding-cuts (Plate 15, Fig. 2), and clean off.
6. Fold handle and silver-solder internal angles.
7. Fit handle to body and silver-solder both joints at one firing (Plate 39, Fig. 2).

8. Grind top of jug flat.

9. Finish all surfaces and polish.

EXAMPLE No. 36.   HOT-WATER JUG (Plates 63 and 74)

1. Proceed as for example No. 35, Paragraphs 1–3.

The elevation drawing from which the pattern is made should be $\frac{3}{32}$ inch narrower than the required finished size.

2. Grind top flat.

3. Cut and fit No. 19 S.W.G. sheet-metal top, allowing a projection at the handle end, which will form the top surface of the upper handle-socket.

4. File bevel on one edge of length of $\frac{3}{16} \times \frac{3}{32}$ inch strip, bend to circle and silver-solder butt joint.

5. Mark exact location of circle on the top and silver-solder.

6. Remove waste inside the circle with piercing-saw and clean off the cut edge.

7. Mark ovoid spout-opening on the top and cut $\frac{1}{16}$ inch inside the line.

8. Silver-solder top to body.

9. Clean off edges, finish spout-opening and top of upper handle-socket.

10. Cut and assemble three sides of upper handle-socket (Plate 39, Fig. 5).

11. Cut and assemble complete lower handle-socket (Plate 39, Fig. 5).

12. Mark locations and silver-solder handle-sockets to body. (The fourth side of the upper one is the extension of the top.)

13. Hollow and planish lid (with small flat for knob seating) and finish edge.

14. Cut, bend and silver-solder circle of $\frac{1}{8} \times \frac{1}{16}$ inch strip, which is an easy push fit in body.

15. Silver-solder to lid.

16. Make (Plate 40) and silver-solder applied hinge (Plate 40, Fig. 6, *b*) to lid and body. A recess is filed in the edge of the lid to accommodate one side of hinge.

17. Clean off all joints, prepare and polish surfaces.

18. Cut and finish handle in ebony or black vulcanized fibre and fit to sockets by draw-pinning (Plate 34).

19. Hand turn, file up and finish knob.

20. Silver-solder $\frac{1}{4}$ inch length of $\frac{1}{4}$ inch round rod to length of 4 B.A. screwed rod and file ball-ended bolt-head.

21. Fix knob to lid by 4 B.A. wing-nut made from $\frac{1}{16}$ inch metal.

EXAMPLE No. 37. TEAPOT (Plates 62 and 74)

The construction is exactly similar to example No. 36 except that the waste metal behind the spout is not removed, but continues up to the under face of the top, to which it is silver-soldered when the top is jointed. Its area is drilled in a triangle of $\frac{5}{32}$ inch holes, which form a strainer. The holes are arranged in horizontal diminishing rows and should be as near together as the strength of the intervening bridges of metal will permit.

Instead of circular lids and body openings to the hot-water jug and teapot, they may be constructed as hexagons, if preferred. In that case the $\frac{3}{16} \times \frac{3}{32}$ inch strip should be assembled as a mitred hexagon instead of a circle (Example No. 36, Paragraphs 4, 5 and 6).

The lids must be panelled in six flat sloping faces. They are cut and hollowed as circles and then annealed. The panelling lines are set out and the faces worked flat by lightly hammering on the end grain of a piece of hardwood which is cut to the shape of one face. This will produce a form of approximate shape with slightly rounded corners. The lid is again annealed and the inside lightly smeared with oil. It is then filled with pitch and plaster-of-paris and inverted on a pitch-block (a wooden tray filled with the mixture) or on a pitch-bowl. This procedure ensures that no air-spaces exist between the under face of the lid and the pitch. The faces are now planished, trued and the corners formed by the intersection of the faces are worked sharp and quite straight. (A small flat is worked to provide a seating for the knob.) The lid is removed from the pitch and the hexagonal outline set out, cut and the edge trued and finished. The $\frac{1}{8} \times \frac{1}{16}$ inch strip is also assembled and silver-soldered to the lid as a mitred hexagon (Example No. 36, Paragraphs 14 and 15).

EXAMPLE No. 38. TEAPOT STAND (Plates 62 and 74)

A stand may be simply made by silver-soldering mitred hexagons of $\frac{3}{16}$-inch astragal moulding and $\frac{1}{4} \times \frac{1}{8}$ inch (or $\frac{3}{16} \times \frac{3}{32}$ inch) strip metal to a base of No. 19 S.W.G. sheet metal. It may be 5 inches across the flats.

EXAMPLE No. 39. FRUIT STAND (Plates 64 and 75)

1. Raise with mallet and planish bowl in No. 19 S.W.G. sheet metal. (Alternatively it may be hollowed.)

2. Silver-solder $\frac{1}{8}$ inch half round wire under the edge. Clean off and finish edge with slight upper rounding.

3. Raise stem of mounting with raising-hammer in No. 18 S.W.G. sheet metal, contract to the required diameter and remove waste centre. (This member could also be shaped by seaming and silver-soldering two cones together at their smaller ends and then contracting to the required diameter at the narrowest part, finally stretching the ends to complete the profile.)

4. Finish edges, contract the turned-down rims or fillets and grind the edges flat and exactly parallel with each other.

5. Raise and finish the collet (or upper member) in the same way. Alternatively it may be shaped from a seamed cone (Plate 6, Fig. 8).

6. Raise (or hollow) and planish the upper and lower members of knop (or centre of mounting), stretch and finish edges and drill a $\frac{1}{4}$ inch hole in the centre of each.

7. Silver-solder length of $\frac{3}{16}$ inch half-round wire to length of $\frac{1}{4} \times \frac{1}{8}$ inch metal, then bend to circle and silver-solder butt joint.

8. Assemble knop and lightly clamp together with length of No. 2 B.A. screwed rod (through holes) and two nuts. Adjust and silver-solder the edge joints and remove the screw clamp.

9. Raise (or hollow) and finish base, in No. 18 S.W.G. sheet metal and remove waste centre with piercing-saw.

10. Round, bend and silver-solder base-ring in $\frac{1}{4} \times \frac{1}{8}$ inch metal and silver-solder to base.

11. Silver-solder collet to knop.

12. Silver-solder knop to stem.

13. Silver-solder stem to base.

14. Bend edgewise and silver-solder circle of $\frac{1}{8} \times \frac{1}{16}$ inch strip metal, which is a tight push fit inside the upper fillet of collet, to provide a wide bearing surface for bowl joint.

15. Fit and silver-solder completed mounting to bowl.

16. Clean off all edge joints true and square with safe-edged files, finishing with fine emery-cloth.

17. Prepare and finish surfaces and polish.

Attention should be paid to the final circularity and truth of the components of the mounting and great care is required to ensure the parallelism of their upper and lower edges before jointing, as comparatively small errors in levelling will be magnified at the edge of the bowl.

CHAPTER XXX

THE TEACHING OF HAMMERED METALWORK

Hand Craft in Education—General or Formal Metalwork—Light Metalwork—Hammered Metalwork—Organization and Teaching Method—Workshop Equipment—Type of Work—Courses of Work—The Aims of a Course of Hand Craft—The Introductory Course—Design of Examples of Work in an Introductory Course—The Advanced Course—Demonstrations—Theory—Drawing—Co-operation and Correlation—Craft Standard.

TRAINING in hand craft is provided in a well-balanced curriculum of a modern school. Such training is not intended to be directly vocational. It is concerned with the expansion of the constructive tendencies, the co-ordination of mind and hand, the creation of interests and æsthetic perception. Its aims are to bring a pupil into contact with activities of everyday life, to stimulate the desire to do and to make, to give skill for accomplishment and to impart an appreciation of design as a basis for self-expression.

The realization of the contribution which hand craft can make in the development of a young pupil has steadily gained ground during the last fifty years, so that to-day few schools omit this training in some form from the curriculum.

Moreover, it is recognized that a liberal education considers the arousing of interests during school life which will continue, and among these are the hobbies which result directly from training in hand craft. Creation of interests and the provision of constructive ability for the employment of leisure is an aspect of education which is becoming increasingly important.

Those familiar with the work of the schools are bound to admit that hand craft training has generally reached a high standard of excellence. The practical-room crafts of book-binding, metalwork, science handwork, weaving, leatherwork, basketry, etc., are carried out efficiently with a relatively simple equipment and teachers are usually able to instruct their pupils after either college or locally arranged courses.

For more advanced pupils, instruction to a workshop standard in woodwork and metalwork, also gardening and rural hand crafts in country districts, are provided for boys and training in the House-crafts for girls. These activities make greater demands upon the craft-skill of the teacher and require a larger and more expensive equipment.

In the case of boys' workshop crafts, development has been greater in woodwork than in metalwork, though it cannot be denied that craftwork in metal offers the same educational facilities as that in wood. It is probable that the future will see a further widening of the field of educational hand craft and that a considerable advance both in the type of metalwork course adopted and in the craft standard reached will be made.

GENERAL OR FORMAL METALWORK

In contrast with woodwork, possessing relatively few processes, and which requires a compact and standardized equipment, general metalwork has several branches, each having specialized processes and technique. Most of the basic tool-operations of woodwork are common to all branches of craftwork in wood, so that the main processes of pattern-making, cabinet-making, carpentry and joinery are virtually the same. A hole, for example, is bored by similar methods in each of the foregoing branches of woodwork and many of their joints and constructional arrangements are identical. In this respect metalwork is more complex and the methods of cutting, shaping and jointing in one of its branches are often totally inapplicable to the others. In addition, the processes of metalwork frequently vary with different metals, as, for example, the jointing methods of brass and aluminium.

The main branches of general metal work as an educational hand craft subject may be broadly classified as follows:—

1. *Bench or Vice Work*

The cutting, shaping, fitting and jointing processes of work in iron, steel and non-ferrous metal for which a bench and vice are used:—

2. *Sheet Metalwork*

The processes of sheet metalwork are in three groups:—
(*a*) Work in sheet iron and sheet steel.
(*b*) Tinplate work.
(*c*) Hammered metalwork—or the hand processes of silversmithing applied to the non-ferrous base metals.

3. *Forge Work*

    (*a*) Shaping operations at red heat and welding of iron and mild steel.
    (*b*) Annealing, shaping, hardening and tempering of tool-steel.

4. *Machine Work*

    (*a*) Hand-turning of non-ferrous metal and non-metallic materials.
    (*b*) Shaping of sheet metal by spinning.
    (*c*) Metal turning and general lathe work.
    (*d*) The operations of simple machine tools.

Where facilities exist in a well-fitted school workshop, it is desirable that a course of metalwork for senior boys should provide experience in the elements of the four main branches, avoiding specialization until the end of a year's course at least, in which has been included the basic processes of each branch, with the exception of machine work in the case of younger pupils.

Each branch of metalwork requires its own tools and apparatus, and the cost of providing even a nucleus equipment to enable a comprehensive course to be arranged in a school workshop has, in many instances, proved prohibitive.

It often becomes necessary to select a type of metalwork within the limit of initial expenditure which will provide the best training in design and craftsmanship.

Machine work is at once discounted for reasons of cost.

Forge work may be desirable, but requires the installation of expensive apparatus and one forge can only accommodate four pupils at most.

Tinplate work is useful in that it forms a cheap introduction to sheet metalwork in general and the operation of soft-soldering in particular. It is not, however, suited to form the sole activity of a school metalwork course, as tinplate is not an appropriate material in which to execute any advanced work. Tinsmithing is a craft requiring long practice if the surface of the metal is to be preserved and the finished work is to appear worth the work involved.

The same is true of hammered metalwork unless preceded by more formal metalwork where young pupils are concerned.

Bench work in iron and steel has many invaluable and fundamental processes from the teaching point of view, which should be included in any metalwork course, though a long course of this work does not usually develop a pupil's artistic talent as much as is desirable, nor does it provide the best facilities for the teaching of constructive design.

LIGHT METALWORK

When cost is a restricting factor, an arrangement is outlined which may be termed Light Metalwork. Processes of the various branches of general metalwork are included which, it is suggested, will together form a useful course, using minimum equipment.

A room or workshop fitted with rigid benches and a $3\frac{1}{2}$ inch vice for each pupil is assumed. (The type of metalwork which is attempted on trestle tables is so seldom satisfactory that in view of the demands made upon the time-table by other subjects, it would hardly appear to be justified, as it does not make sufficient contribution to a pupil's education to warrant its teaching time.)

The equipment should consist of the essential hand tools for the basic processes of bench work and sheet metalwork. It must include a blowpipe and soldering-hearth, also the necessary heavy stakes. A course of light metalwork involves:—

1. The chief processes of bench work in iron and steel, for example, setting-out, cutting, straight, curved and bevel filing, cold bending, drilling, riveting, hand screwcutting, surface filing and polishing.

2. The more important processes of tinplate work:—setting-out, cutting, bending, folding and seaming. The jointing process of soft-soldering. Edge-folding and edge-wiring.

3. Simple light forge work using a blowpipe, soldering-hearth and a small anvil. Spreading, drawing-down of flat and circular tapers, hot bending, twisting, annealing, hardening and tempering of tool-steel. The jointing process of brazing.

Introductory work consists of very simple examples designed to embody the foregoing processes. This may conveniently consist of elementary tool-making for groups 1 and 3 and the second is covered by the inclusion of simple folded and circular trays and perhaps a funnel or canister in tinplate. Simplicity, good design and the progressive inclusion of the processes are of first importance.

Later advanced work may then take the form of hammered metalwork.

HAMMERED METALWORK

This branch of sheet metalwork is proving increasingly useful as an educational craft. It requires neither machine equipment nor an expensively fitted workshop and its demands in the matter of tools and apparatus are reasonable.

Provided that the course of work is constructive, it fulfils the conditions necessary for training in hand craft and design to the standard generally accepted.

ORGANIZATION AND TEACHING METHOD

Suggestions for the teaching of hammered metalwork are given, though the method advanced is by no means new. General principles, upon which many successful teachers of hand craft have based their work, are applied to this craft in particular.

Hammered metalwork may be taught as a separate craft in its own workshop in College, Technical, Art and Craft, Secondary, Central and Senior Elementary Schools and conducted on similar lines to those of the teaching of woodwork. This is the best organization, as a workshop will then be fitted expressly for the teaching of the one craft. No special arrangement is necessary and the only essential fittings are a gas service pipe and sink with running water. Rigid bench accommodation is always necessary, which can be arranged for convenience of teaching and demonstration, provided that sufficient floor-space exists. Twenty pupils are the maximum number that can be taught efficiently by one teacher. If thirty pupils are taught, as in some Secondary School workshops at present, it is not reasonable to expect a high standard of craftsmanship, nor that the teaching can be really effective. When a simple course of work involving the basic processes has been completed, the more advanced work will then be constructive 'silversmithing' in gilding-metal, copper and brass. (No difficulty is usually experienced in recovering the cost of material for this more advanced work from pupils in average financial circumstances.)

An alternative consists in the teaching of hammered metalwork as an auxiliary craft to follow or run parallel with a course in woodwork. It then forms a second workshop craft which may be taken by pupils who have completed a woodwork course, or it may be taught at the same time as woodwork to pupils selected for additional craft training. The scope of the work will be restricted, owing to mutual interference. The workshop is fitted for the teaching of woodwork and provision made for a number of bench places for metalwork, using simple equipment. In these circumstances, the work must consist of a simpler course which embodies the main processes and tool operations and gives some practice in elementary constructive work.

The craft may also form part of the activities of a Senior School practical room, in which case it shares the workroom with other crafts.

In spite of the fact that only the simplest equipment need be used, some sound fundamental work may be produced under these conditions.

For various reasons senior girls have not usually in the past used a school workshop. It is, however, nowadays increasingly common to find girls receiving some training in the use of simple household tools, and in some cases constructive woodwork is taught. It is probable that this may lead to the inclusion of a workshop craft for girls in addition to, or as an alternative to, those taught at present. The lighter side of hammered metalwork (as distinct from jewellery and work in wire) is well within the capabilities of senior girls. Many fine examples of advanced work in metal are being executed in Art and Craft Schools by girls and women students.

WORKSHOP EQUIPMENT

Provided that the necessary minimum of hand tools and large stakes exist, much of the smaller specialized equipment may be made in the workshop. In many instances wood hollowing and shaping blocks, punches and wiring tools, cannot be bought, and it is always more satisfactory to make these small tools, which can then be designed and constructed exactly to suit their specialized purpose. It is frequently necessary to construct teaching and demonstration equipment, also apparatus which will simplify the working of a difficult process or operation for a class of pupils. Under this heading are objects unknown to a working craftsman in metal, but which are invaluable to a craftsman engaged in teaching. If cost is an important consideration, much of the more expensive equipment, such as a surface-plate, small stakes and hammers, may be successfully improvised and adapted. It is realised that the fitting-up of a school workshop for the teaching of hammered metalwork makes considerable demands upon the skill and ingenuity of a keen craft teacher, the exercise of which is by no means confined to the hours of instruction.

TYPE OF WORK

The type of metalwork under consideration is not a newcomer to the wide field of educational activities. It has been taught for some years as

Repoussé and 'Beaten metalwork.' In the main, the work has been decorative rather than constructive. To be of real value educationally, a craft should be definitely constructive, in order to provide valuable and necessary training in design.

A constructive craft is concerned with the designing and making of a finished example of work, in which decoration assists or supports but is subordinate to the construction. In Repoussé the 'cart' of decoration precedes the 'horse' of construction. There is more to be gained, educationally, in the designing and making of a perfectly plain tankard, for instance, than in the modelling of an elaborate panel in Repoussé which is put into a frame and used as a fire-screen.

It should not be inferred that the varied tool-operations and processes of constructive work in hammered metal are so complex or difficult that they are incapable of being executed to a reasonable standard by a boy, nor yet that any contracted method or short cut can be introduced in the teaching. A young pupil's skill and proficiency in this, as in any craft, can only be acquired with practice and as a result of thorough teaching, with ample demonstration of the correct use of the tools.

Courses of Work

To enable the teaching of a craft to be arranged easily and progressively it is necessary that a course of work should be decided upon before teaching is commenced.

The Aims of a Course of Hand Craft

The aims in formulating a course of hand craft should be:—

1. To include the teaching of the fundamental tool-operations and processes by as direct a method as possible.

2. To provide practice and experience in the application of the fundamentals, to work of good design and sound construction.

The course must be based on the age and ability of the pupils and also on the time available, and it is suggested that it is divided into two parts which, for convenience, may be called introductory and advanced.

The Introductory Course

This part of the instruction should consist of perhaps six simple examples of finished work, the making of which embodies the main tool-operations and processes in a progressive arrangement. Practice in the principal processes of setting-out, cutting, surface-preparation, bending, folding, hollowing, sinking, stretching and planishing, also the jointing processes of soft- and silver-soldering, should be included in the simplest work possible.

This course should be taken by all the pupils at the commencement of work in the craft. It should be very carefully formulated, consisting of essentials only, and should be regarded as the important foundation upon which later work is built. Upon its suitability, the success or failure of the teaching of the craft will depend.

Its purpose is to ensure that all the necessary processes are learned in due order, and a pupil who misses any stage of the instruction will be handicapped later on by the omission. Once decided upon, it will be well to adhere to it, not permitting much variation. There is no purpose in allowing freedom to the pupils at this stage, when the only freedom they can take is the freedom to make mistakes and perpetuate errors.

The course would naturally be varied or modified with fresh classes, taking advantage of experience gained with previous ones.

The introductory course should therefore be rigid—mainly class work and demonstration by the teacher.

DESIGN OF EXAMPLES OF WORK IN AN INTRODUCTORY COURSE

The responsibility for the design of each example of work in an introductory course rests with the teacher. Self-expression is not considered at this stage. It is not applicable in the elementary work of a subject such as this, which is possessed of a well-defined technique. A pupil must have knowledge of the processes and some experience in the handling of the material before he is in a position to express any ideas he may have, or even have ideas which are worthy of expression.

When arranging an introductory course, it is suggested that a list be made of what are considered to be the essential tool-operations and processes, graded in order of difficulty and in a natural progression. Sketches are then made of the simplest examples of work which will embody the requirements of the list, avoiding any undue repetition. Napkin rings, caddy-spoons, small trays and bowls, teapot stands, vases, inkstands, unhinged boxes and the like, lend themselves to such a variety of simple treatment that it is usually a comparatively easy matter to arrange an introductory course with the tool-operations and processes in any desired order.

When the course has been finally decided upon, working drawings are made and then each example should be constructed by the teacher with as much care and attention to detail as possible. The complete course so made, besides revealing any unsuspected difficulties, is invaluable in teaching demonstrations, the excellence of its craftsmanship being an incentive to careful and thorough work. A craft teacher receives in direct proportion as he gives. If good work is demonstrated and shown, the pupil's effort will be proportionately good.

When designing any example of work for such a course, it is wise to examine its full-sized drawing and to obtain satisfactory answers to such questions as the following:

1. Does it provide adequate practice in the required process ?
2. Will it do its particular job properly ?
3. Is its material suitable ?
4. Are its proportions correct and pleasing ?
5. Is its construction sound ?
6. Will it be pleasant to handle ?
7. Does its decoration, if any, support its construction ?
8. Has it an attractive appearance, and is due restraint in decoration exercised ?

Before these simple obligations are met, it is sometimes necessary to introduce modifications in the original plan that will improve its design or remove some hitherto unnoticed defect which would mar its appearance or detract from the utility of the finished work.

When the complete course has been so designed, it should be examined collectively:—

1. Has sufficient work been included for the time available ?
2. Has time been allowed for the necessary demonstration, theory and drawing ?
3. Has any essential process been omitted ?
4. Is any particular operation over-emphasized ?
5. Is the standard of difficulty correct for the age and ability of the pupils taking the course ?
6. Will the course as a whole be attractive ?

Exercises need seldom be given as such. Simple finished work can usually be designed which embodies two or more basic processes in the correct sequence.

It is generally desirable that examples of work in an introductory course shall be complete in themselves, avoiding objects which have to be fastened on to something else and which require to be designed expressly for their surroundings.

THE ADVANCED COURSE

The advanced course which follows should be flexible, and may be arranged to suit individual requirements. At this stage the pupils will be familiar with the tools and will have had some experience of the fundamental processes of the introductory course.

Work is now included which provides experience in the processes of contracting, raising of small simple forms, treatment of edges and more advanced jointing operations.

The teaching of design becomes an important part of the work of this course, interlacing with the advancement of the tool-operations and processes of the introductory course. At first, suggestions from the pupils are invited, examined, adapted and incorporated. Questions of decoration, its suitability, subordination and restraint, are considered. Finally the pupils are given the requirements for a particular example of work and, using these, they submit a suggestion in the form of a sketch. From this they make the simple full-sized working drawing and then proceed to the construction.

Individual work will characterize the advanced course, class demonstrations being restricted to fresh processes.

DEMONSTRATIONS

Thorough class demonstrations of the processes and tool-operations are absolutely necessary in the early stages. A teacher of hand craft, who is not himself a competent craftsman, may but accompany his pupils. He cannot lead them.

THEORY

A short but sufficient time must be devoted to theory to enable pupils to understand correctly the action of the tools and the underlying principles of the processes. To know 'how and why it works' is a vital necessity to a boy, if his interest is to be maintained and also if he is to become independent of rule-of-thumb methods.

DRAWING

There is an irreducible minimum of technical drawing, as necessary to the teaching of hammered metalwork as a chart is to a navigator. Rough dimensioned sketches, which may (or may not) serve in woodwork, are valueless in this craft as working drawings. Wood is shaped by a removal of waste from its original volume. It is never shaped by stretching, contracting or raising processes which involve a total re-arrangement of the material. A full-sized drawing (from which can be plotted the commencing shape and size of the material), whilst not perhaps always necessary in woodwork, is essential in work in sheet metal. A dimensioned sketch does not readily indicate proportion, which in hammered metalwork is often confined within narrow limits.

The general requirements in drawing are met by the ordinary full-sized plan and elevation projection. Sectional elevations are extremely useful, and sufficient plane and solid geometry is required to enable correct patterns to be produced. For younger pupils, these necessary patterns may be made by the teacher as class demonstrations.

CO-OPERATION AND CORRELATION

Design emerges from construction. The craft teacher is, therefore, a teacher of design, the two being inseparable, and it is of vital importance that a wide and generous appreciation of good design is combined with executive skill.

Insularity has, in the past, detracted from the value of craft teaching. Art and hand craft have often been taught as entirely separate subjects, instead of in a closely interwoven alliance. Many teachers of excellent craftsmanship have had no opportunity for an art training and their good taste has not been developed. Neither have they consistently asked for guidance from their art colleagues, perhaps because of a mistaken feeling of inferiority or else in fear lest their activities should be controlled from the art room. When co-operation has been sought, the assistance given has, in unfortunate instances, been of no practical value, as the suggestions offered showed little understanding of either craft processes, limitations of materials or craft capabilities of pupils. Hand craft and art have, therefore, run on separate, though parallel lines with comparatively little merging. The teaching of hand craft has suffered thereby, craft-skill being far in advance of artistic merit in the work produced, because mere technical processes and their application have been taught without the restraining and refining influences of a training in art. (In this connection the use of the term 'art training' implies that which ultimately produces good taste. Training which encourages the abominations that so blatantly masquerade as art is neither included nor considered.)

The most successful craft-teacher is the craftsman who is also an artist, competent to direct his teaching into channels of good design.

For the less fortunate—and there are many who through no fault have not this ability—it becomes necessary to co-operate very closely with the art staff in the design of their work. From the craftsman is demanded a willingness to incorporate suggestions, and from the artist, a conversance with craft processes and materials so that his help may be effective. What could be more beneficial to the practical work of a school than this co-operation and interchange ?

The successful teacher of hand craft rarely concerns himself to-day with what used to be known as correlation. If full advantage is taken of the natural connection existing between hand craft and art, little time is usually available (in the training of senior pupils) for the linking up of hand craft with other subjects. Neither is it generally desirable. Much of the correlated work in schools is valuable provided that it is not considered to be craft training. Its possibilities are often strictly limited and its temporary nature makes a reasonable standard of craftsmanship neither attainable nor necessary. Occasionally work is suggested which allows of the building up of some really constructive effort, mutually beneficial to the teaching of the subjects concerned. More frequently, however, is it the request for work to be undertaken which may be hand craft but which is, nevertheless, totally unsuitable from a teaching point of view. It can seldom take its place in a progressive scheme of craft training and may be the cause of disorganization.

Hand craft should not be regarded as an ' odd-job ' activity. Nowadays it is an established subject, the teaching of which has a well-ordered technique demanding carefully arranged and progressive courses.

CRAFT STANDARD

It is unwise to under-estimate the capabilities of the average pupil and, where a progressive course exists and sufficient time is available, a reasonably high standard of work may, in ordinary circumstances, be expected. Provided that the grammar of the subject has been thoroughly taught in the introductory course, a class or group of pupils is happier when its efforts are fully extended in the attaining of a high standard of execution, than when it works with the realization that a low standard will be accepted.

Conversely, when the standard set is out of reach of the pupils, discouragement and lack of interest will inevitably follow. A stage may be reached when personal assistance by the teacher becomes necessary in order to produce work which involves too difficult tool-operations. This is undesirable and in extreme cases the object and aim of hand-craft training may be lost sight of. Production then takes the place of training and progress becomes sacrificed to showmanship. The scheme of work should be so designed and graded that the whole of the tool-operations may be the unaided work of the pupils as only thus can reliance and self-confidence be created. When the introductory course is satisfactory, the advanced work will follow easily and naturally, allowing the teacher time to concentrate upon the teaching of design and development of good taste and individuality in his pupils.

The opportunities afforded in the teaching of a constructive hand craft for inculcating habits of precision and accuracy are too valuable to be overlooked. Craft training should be characterized by a striving towards precision with an increasing control of tools and material. A craft teacher's conception of accuracy may well be a scale of ascending values, ever rising as experience and confidence are gained by the pupils.

Finally, a wise teacher of hand craft does not make extravagant claims for his subject, nor does he demand that it should have an undue share of the time-table at the expense of other subjects. He does, however, realize the value of the training he gives and knows that it has its definite place in the pupil's development. He teaches constructive hand craft and design to a good standard of execution with a reasonable degree of accuracy and is concerned primarily with the effect of the training on the pupils. He is interested in their individual bias, development and progress rather than in the production of an imposing show of work (in the early stages) or in the alliance of senior school hand craft with subjects other than art.

The teaching method and general presentation of hand craft as an educational subject should be such that, by example and encouragement, thoroughness of effort becomes so attractive that a pupil will be satisfied only with his best. In this way a high standard of excellence becomes his subconscious aim, the realization of which will make its ultimate contribution to the development of his powers of criticism and discrimination. Years hence he may look back at the hours spent in his school workshop where he learned the joy of doing and making, and where his love of a job really well done had its beginnings. He may also have acquired good taste and be attracted to the genuine in design—neither the flimsy and ornate, nor the cumbrous and grotesque—but that which emerges or is developed naturally from technical requirements and constructional essentials. If so, he possesses a cultural attainment which justifies in full the teaching of hand craft in the schools.

COMPARATIVE TEMPERATURES (Approximate)

FUSING POINT	°C.	PROCESS	COLOUR	
Iron	1,500		Blue-white	
Tool Steel	1,400		Brilliant white	
	1,300		White	
	1,200		Yellow	
	1,100		Brilliant orange	Incandescence
Copper	1,085			
Gilding-metal	1,000	Tool-steel	Orange	
Fine Silver	960	Forging		
Yellow Brass	940			
	900		Brilliant red	
Standard Silver	890			
Hard-running Silver-solder	825			
	800	Silver-soldering	Red	
Common Brass	750			
Easy-running Silver-solder	720			
	700	Annealing	Dull red	
	600		Faint red	
Zinc	420			
	360		Blue-grey	
	330		Blue-green	
Lead	325			
	320		Light blue	
	310		Blue	
	300		Dark blue	
	290		Dark purple	
	280		Light purple	
	270	Tool-steel	Brown-purple	Oxidation
	260	Tempering	Brown	
	250		Yellow-brown	
	240		Dark straw	
Tin	235			
	230		Straw	
	220		Pale yellow	
Medium Soft-solder	188	Soft-soldering		
Fine Soft-solder	172			

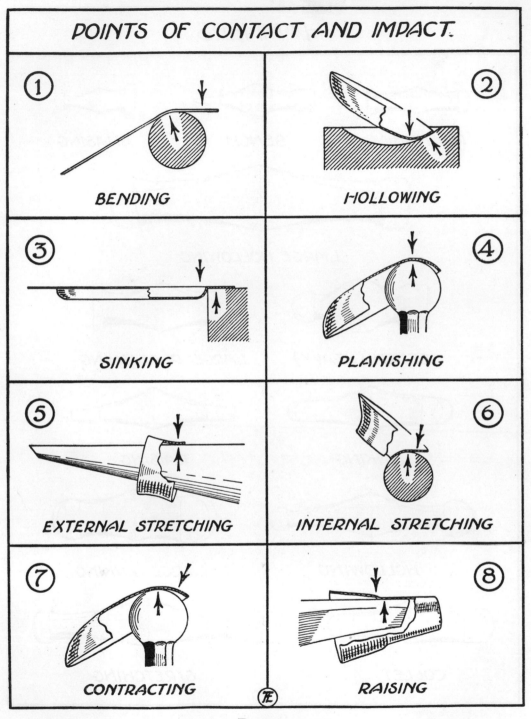

POINTS OF CONTACT AND IMPACT.

1 BENDING

2 HOLLOWING

3 SINKING

4 PLANISHING

5 EXTERNAL STRETCHING

6 INTERNAL STRETCHING

7 CONTRACTING

8 RAISING

PLATE I

197

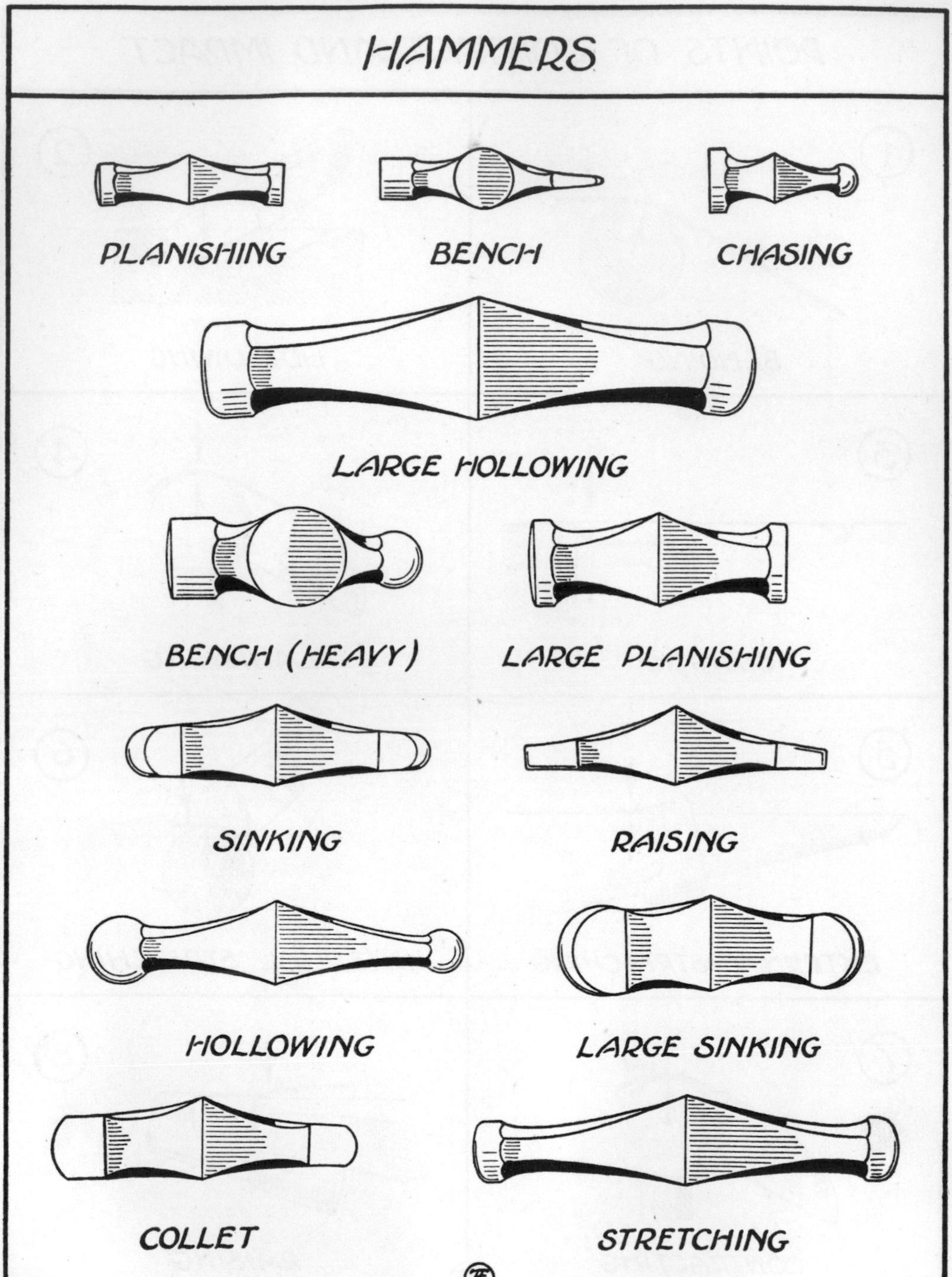

HAMMERS

PLANISHING

BENCH

CHASING

LARGE HOLLOWING

BENCH (HEAVY)

LARGE PLANISHING

SINKING

RAISING

HOLLOWING

LARGE SINKING

COLLET

STRETCHING

PLATE 2

LARGE STAKES.

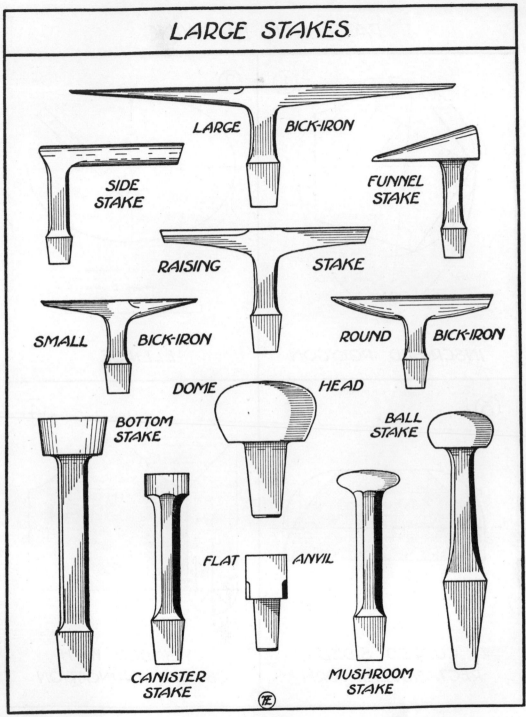

LARGE   BICK-IRON

SIDE STAKE

FUNNEL STAKE

RAISING   STAKE

SMALL   BICK-IRON

ROUND   BICK-IRON

DOME   HEAD

BOTTOM STAKE

BALL STAKE

FLAT   ANVIL

CANISTER STAKE

MUSHROOM STAKE

PLATE 3

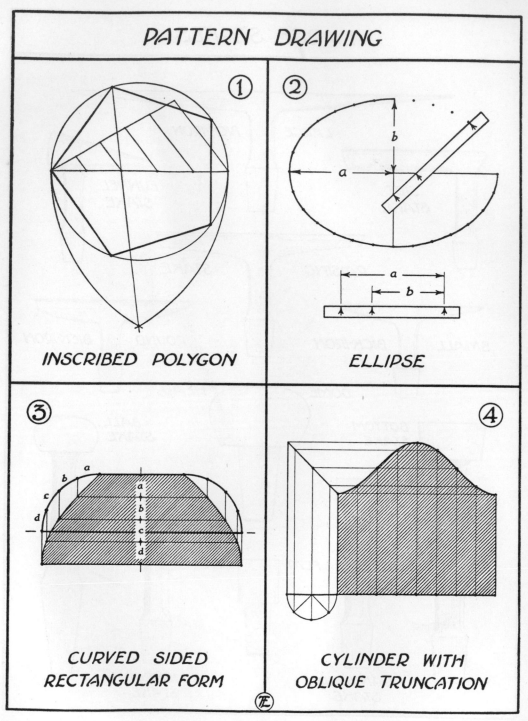

PATTERN DRAWING

① INSCRIBED POLYGON

② ELLIPSE

③ CURVED SIDED RECTANGULAR FORM

④ CYLINDER WITH OBLIQUE TRUNCATION

PLATE 4

200

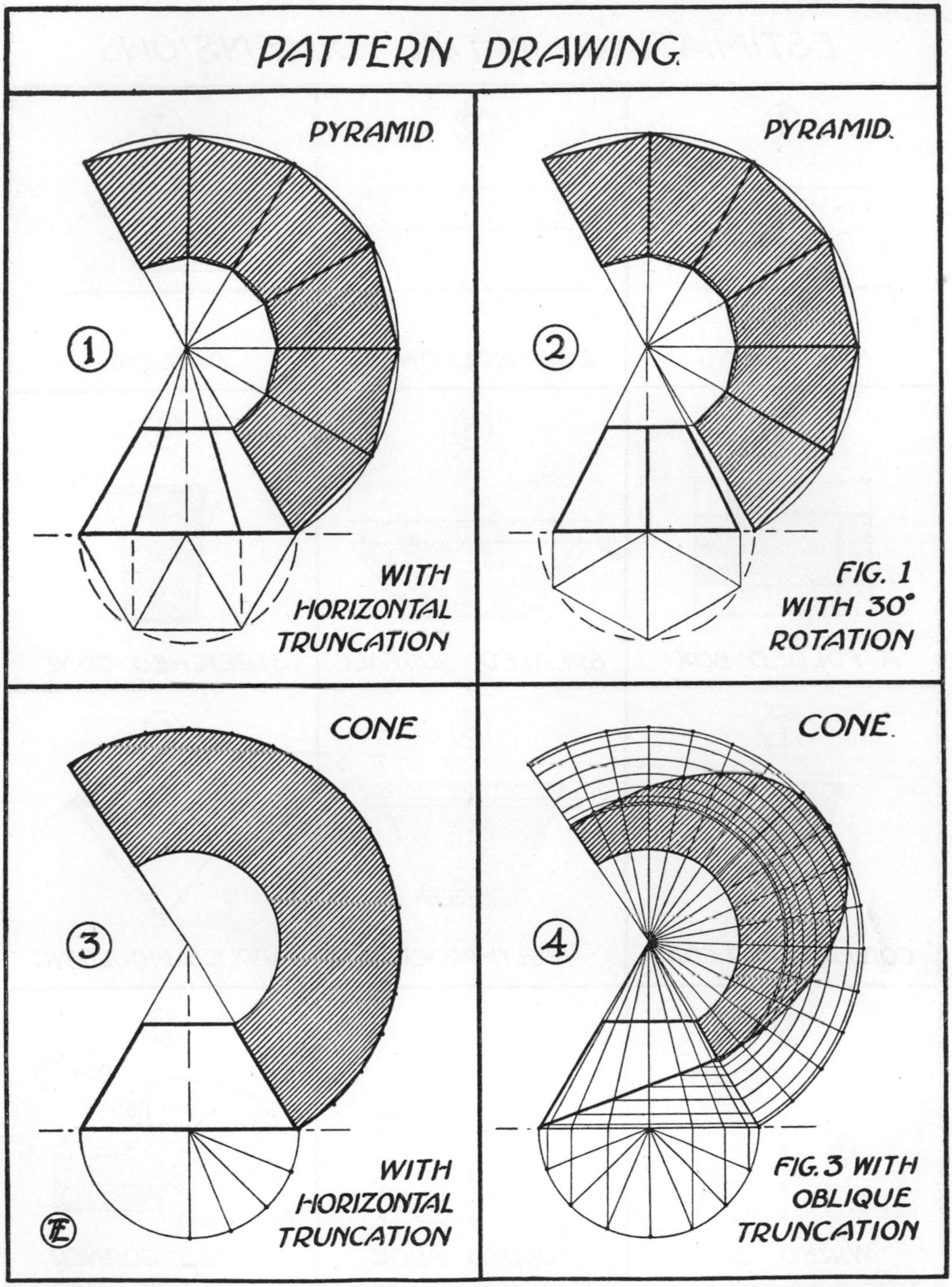

PATTERN DRAWING.

① PYRAMID.
WITH HORIZONTAL TRUNCATION

② PYRAMID.
FIG. 1 WITH 30° ROTATION

③ CONE
WITH HORIZONTAL TRUNCATION

④ CONE.
FIG. 3 WITH OBLIQUE TRUNCATION

PLATE 5

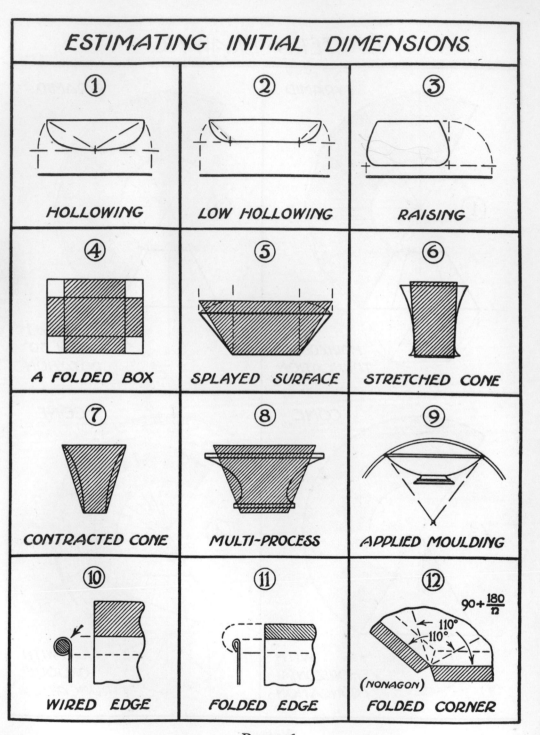

ESTIMATING INITIAL DIMENSIONS.

① HOLLOWING

② LOW HOLLOWING

③ RAISING

④ A FOLDED BOX

⑤ SPLAYED SURFACE

⑥ STRETCHED CONE

⑦ CONTRACTED CONE

⑧ MULTI-PROCESS

⑨ APPLIED MOULDING

⑩ WIRED EDGE

⑪ FOLDED EDGE

⑫ FOLDED CORNER

$90 + \frac{180}{12}$

$110°$

$110°$

(NONAGON)

PLATE 6

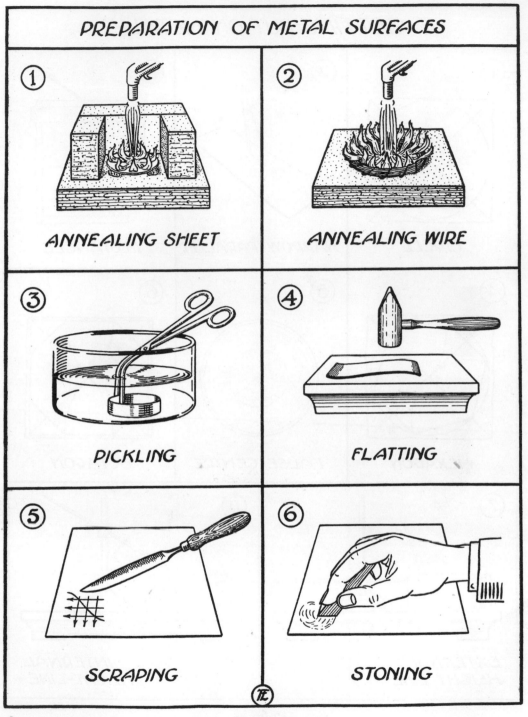

PREPARATION OF METAL SURFACES

① ANNEALING SHEET

② ANNEALING WIRE

③ PICKLING

④ FLATTING

⑤ SCRAPING

⑥ STONING

PLATE 7

203

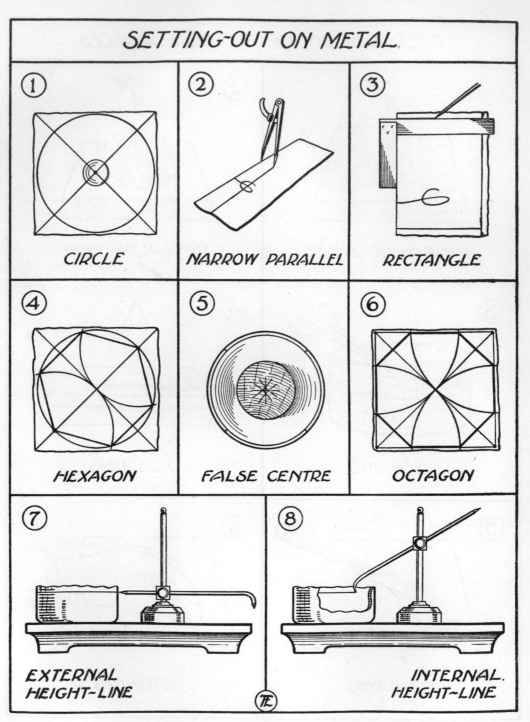

SETTING-OUT ON METAL

① CIRCLE

② NARROW PARALLEL

③ RECTANGLE

④ HEXAGON

⑤ FALSE CENTRE

⑥ OCTAGON

⑦ EXTERNAL HEIGHT-LINE

⑧ INTERNAL HEIGHT-LINE

PLATE 8

204

CUTTING METHODS

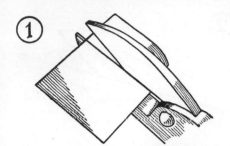

1 A STRAIGHT CUT
WITH STRAIGHT SHEARS

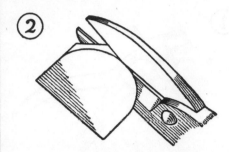

2 AN EXTERNAL CURVE
WITH STRAIGHT SHEARS

3 AN INTERNAL CURVE
WITH CURVED SHEARS

4 A CIRCLE OF THIN STRIP
WITH STRAIGHT SHEARS

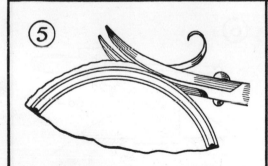

5 A WASTE MARGIN
WITH CURVED SHEARS

6 A SURPLUS EDGE
WITH CURVED SHEARS

PLATE 9

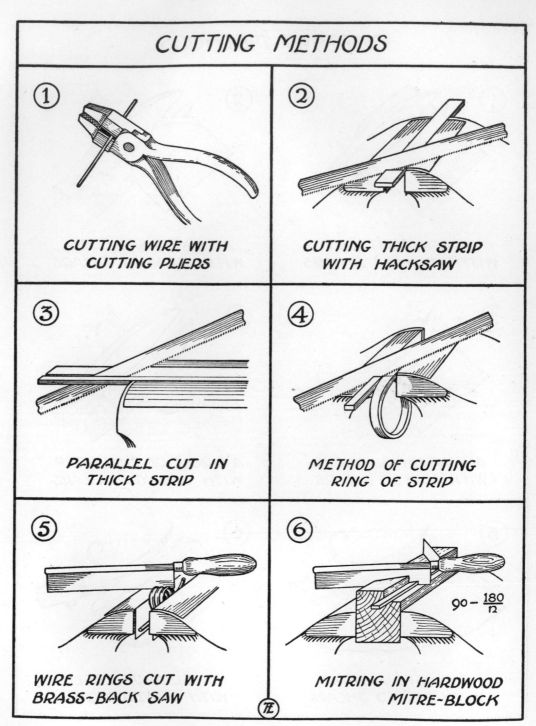

CUTTING METHODS

① CUTTING WIRE WITH CUTTING PLIERS

② CUTTING THICK STRIP WITH HACKSAW

③ PARALLEL CUT IN THICK STRIP

④ METHOD OF CUTTING RING OF STRIP

⑤ WIRE RINGS CUT WITH BRASS-BACK SAW

⑥ MITRING IN HARDWOOD MITRE-BLOCK

$90 - \frac{180}{12}$

PLATE 10

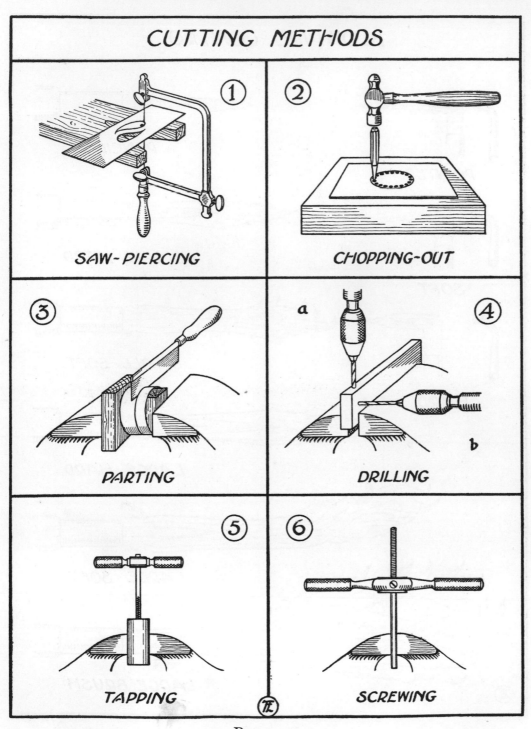

CUTTING METHODS

1. SAW-PIERCING

2. CHOPPING-OUT

3. PARTING

4. DRILLING

5. TAPPING

6. SCREWING

PLATE II

207

BLOWPIPE CONTROL

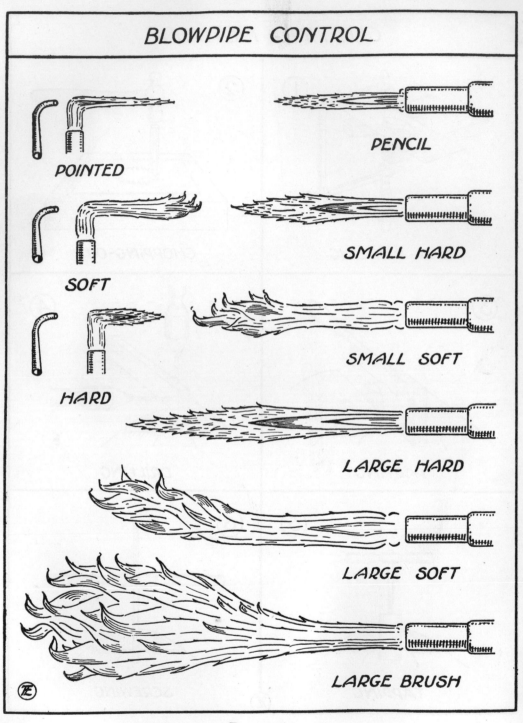

POINTED

PENCIL

SOFT

SMALL HARD

HARD

SMALL SOFT

LARGE HARD

LARGE SOFT

LARGE BRUSH

PLATE 12

BENDING

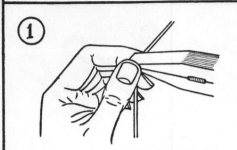

① BENDING A SHARP CORNER IN WIRE WITH FLAT-NOSED PLIERS

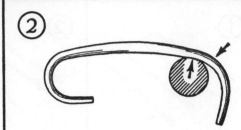

② BENDING A HANDLE BY HAND PRESSURE OR MALLET, ON BAR

③ STAGES IN BENDING WIRE CIRCLE ON CYLINDRICAL FORMER

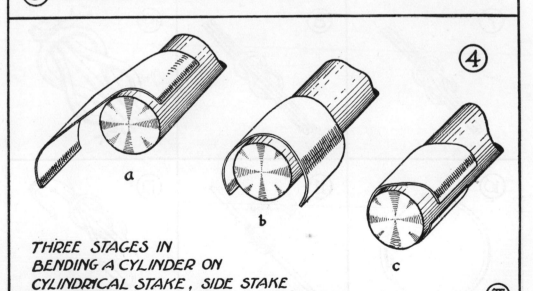

a

b

c

THREE STAGES IN BENDING A CYLINDER ON CYLINDRICAL STAKE, SIDE STAKE OR LENGTH OF MACHINE SHAFTING IN VICE

④

PLATE 13

BENT WIRE HANDLE

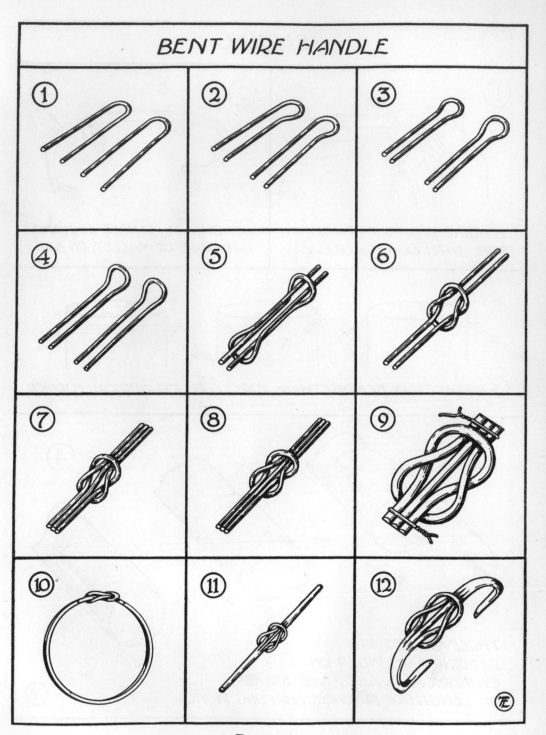

PLATE 14

210

FOLDING

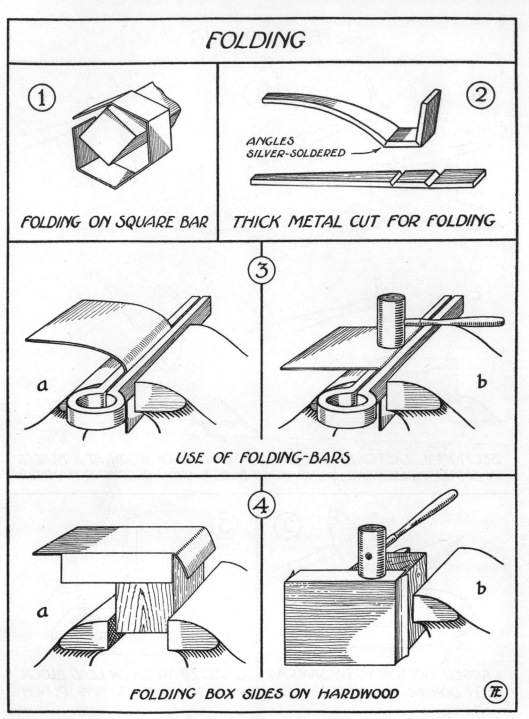

① FOLDING ON SQUARE BAR

② THICK METAL CUT FOR FOLDING
ANGLES SILVER-SOLDERED

③ USE OF FOLDING-BARS
a
b

④ FOLDING BOX SIDES ON HARDWOOD
a
b

PLATE 15

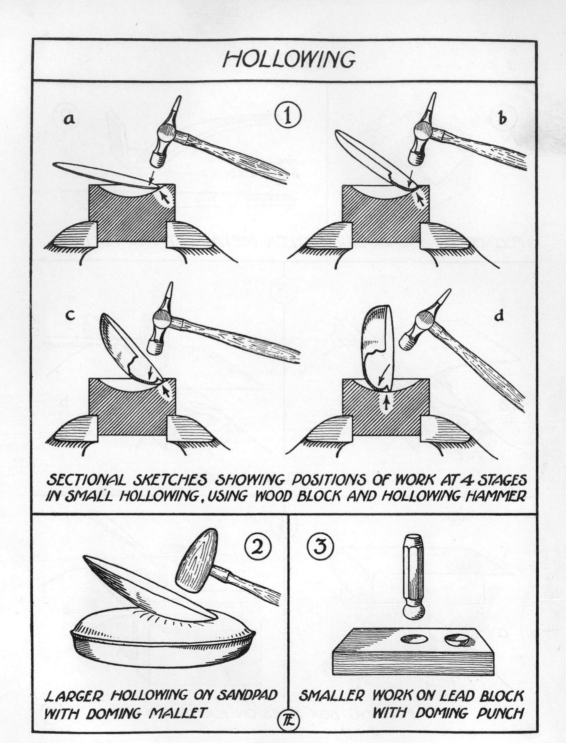

HOLLOWING

(1) a

(1) b

c

d

SECTIONAL SKETCHES SHOWING POSITIONS OF WORK AT 4 STAGES
IN SMALL HOLLOWING, USING WOOD BLOCK AND HOLLOWING HAMMER

(2) LARGER HOLLOWING ON SANDPAD
WITH DOMING MALLET

(3) SMALLER WORK ON LEAD BLOCK
WITH DOMING PUNCH

PLATE 16

212

HOLLOWED FORMS

PLATE 17

213

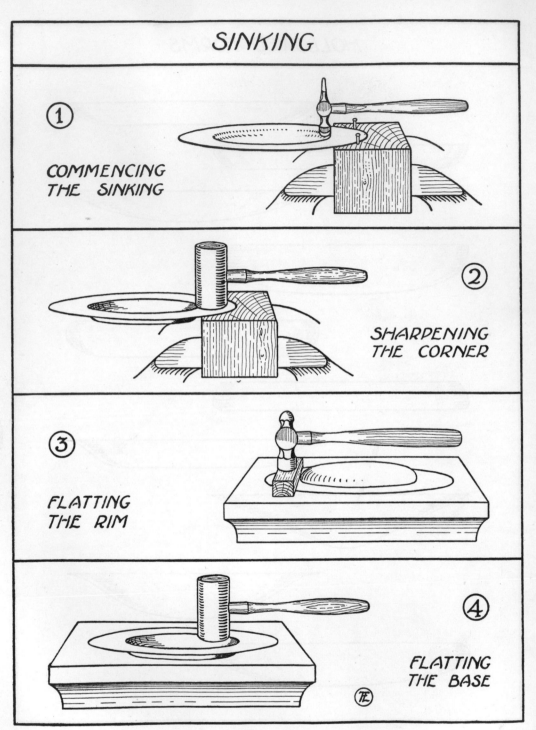

SINKING

1. COMMENCING THE SINKING

2. SHARPENING THE CORNER

3. FLATTING THE RIM

4. FLATTING THE BASE

PLATE 18

214

STRETCHING

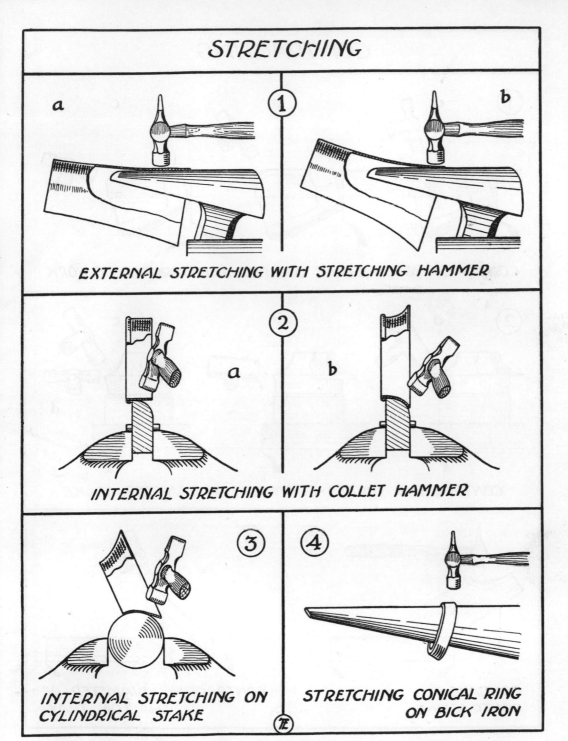

1. EXTERNAL STRETCHING WITH STRETCHING HAMMER

2. INTERNAL STRETCHING WITH COLLET HAMMER

3. INTERNAL STRETCHING ON CYLINDRICAL STAKE

4. STRETCHING CONICAL RING ON BICK IRON

PLATE 19

CONTRACTING.

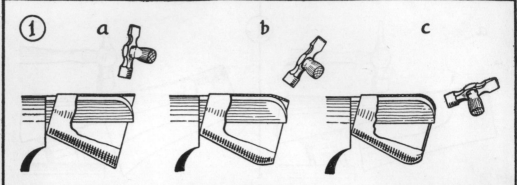

① a b c

CONTRACTING ON STAKE SHAPED TO FIT PROFILE OF WORK

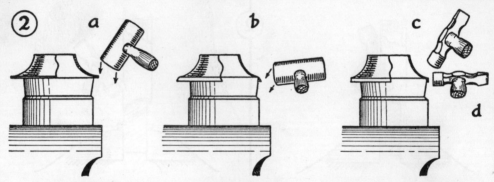

② a b c d

CONTRACTING TURNED-DOWN RIM ON CANISTER STAKE

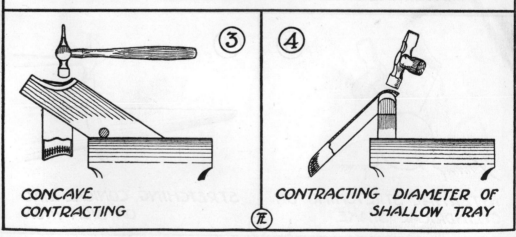

③ ④

CONCAVE CONTRACTING

CONTRACTING DIAMETER OF SHALLOW TRAY

PLATE 20

216

SEAMED FORMS.

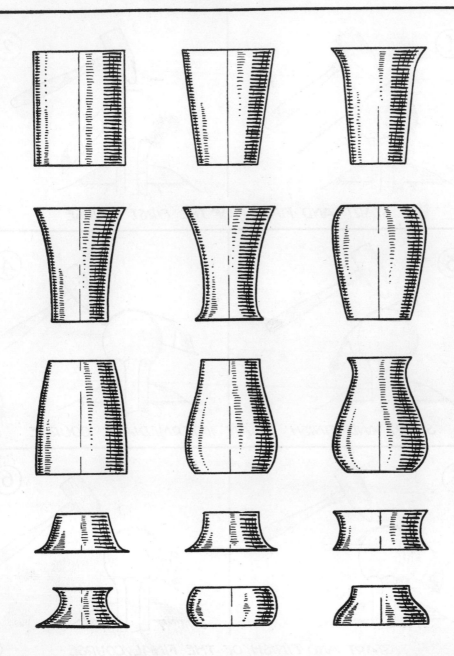

PLATE 21

217

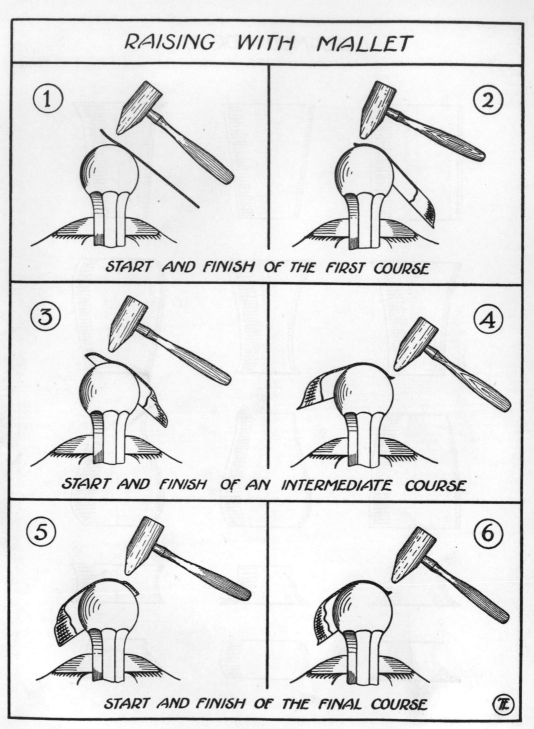

RAISING WITH MALLET

① ②

START AND FINISH OF THE FIRST COURSE

③ ④

START AND FINISH OF AN INTERMEDIATE COURSE

⑤ ⑥

START AND FINISH OF THE FINAL COURSE

PLATE 22

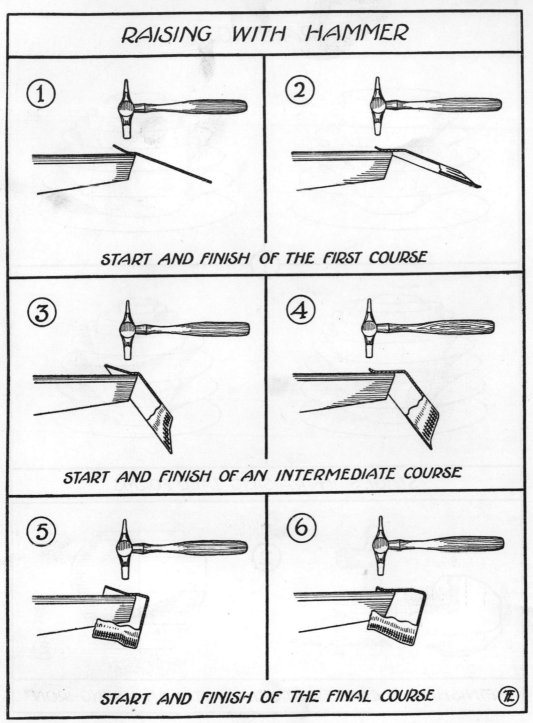

RAISING WITH HAMMER

1 **2**

START AND FINISH OF THE FIRST COURSE

3 **4**

START AND FINISH OF AN INTERMEDIATE COURSE

5 **6**

START AND FINISH OF THE FINAL COURSE

PLATE 23

RAISING.

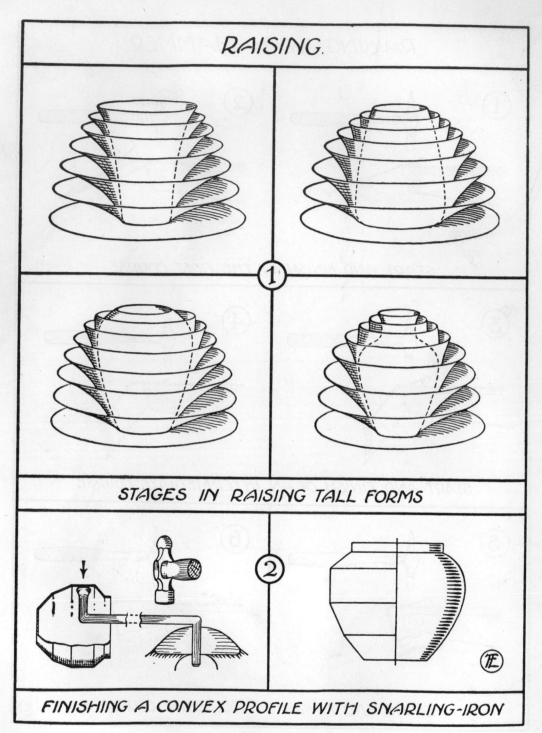

STAGES IN RAISING TALL FORMS

FINISHING A CONVEX PROFILE WITH SNARLING-IRON

PLATE 24

PANELLING.

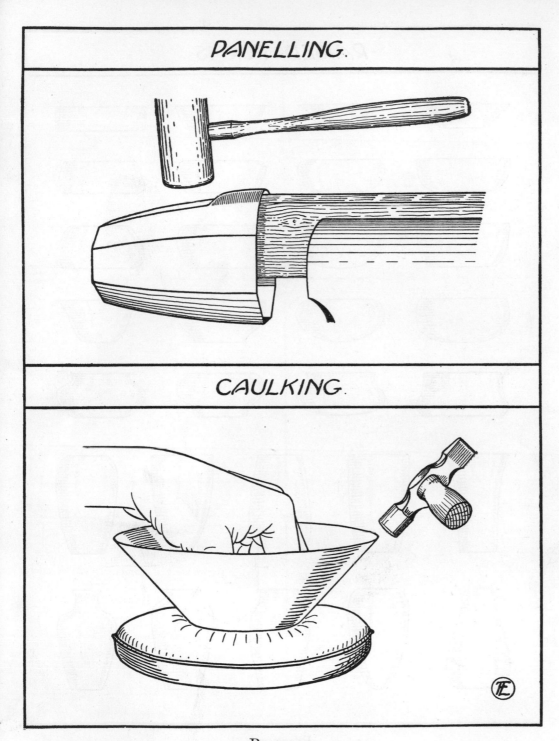

CAULKING.

PLATE 25

221

RAISED FORMS

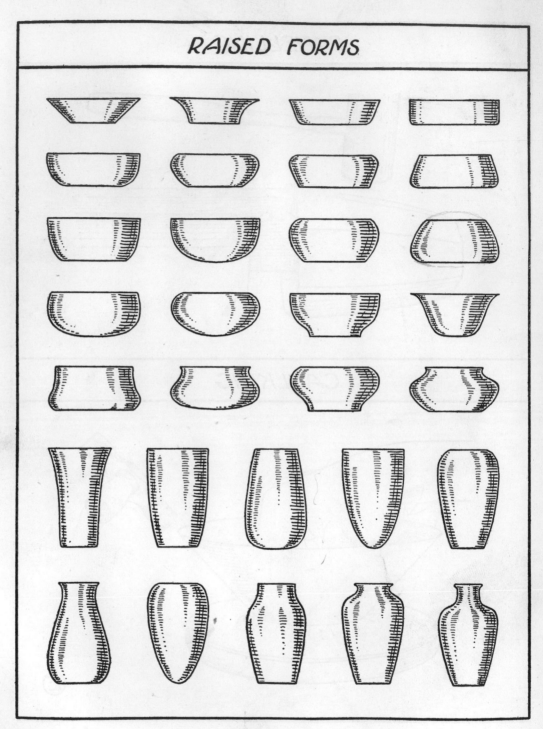

PLATE 26

ACTION OF RAISING PROCESS.

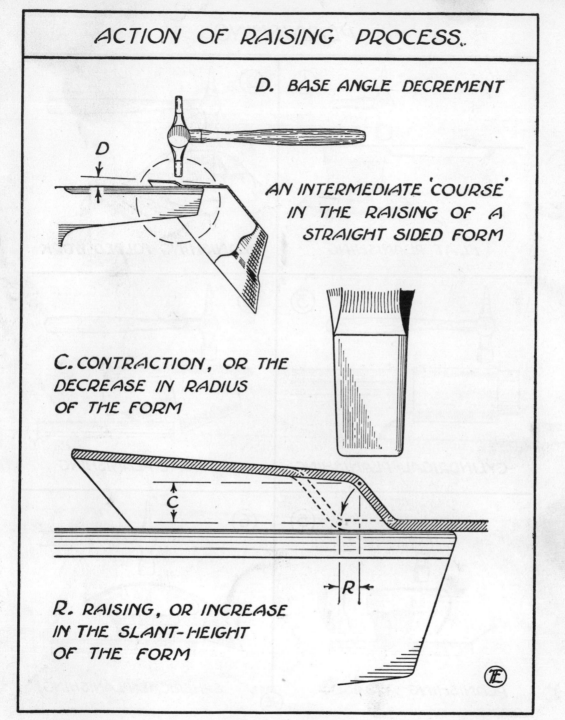

D. BASE ANGLE DECREMENT

AN INTERMEDIATE 'COURSE'
IN THE RAISING OF A
STRAIGHT SIDED FORM

C. CONTRACTION, OR THE
DECREASE IN RADIUS
OF THE FORM

R. RAISING, OR INCREASE
IN THE SLANT-HEIGHT
OF THE FORM

PLATE 27

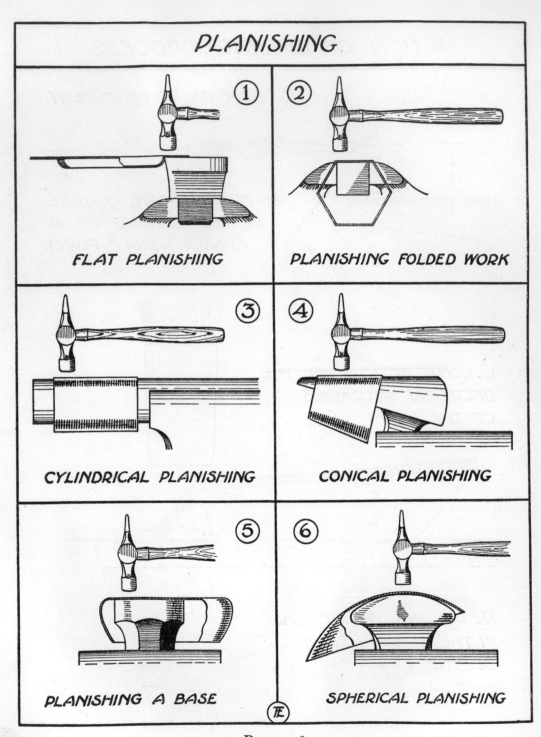

PLANISHING

① FLAT PLANISHING

② PLANISHING FOLDED WORK

③ CYLINDRICAL PLANISHING

④ CONICAL PLANISHING

⑤ PLANISHING A BASE

⑥ SPHERICAL PLANISHING

PLATE 28

224

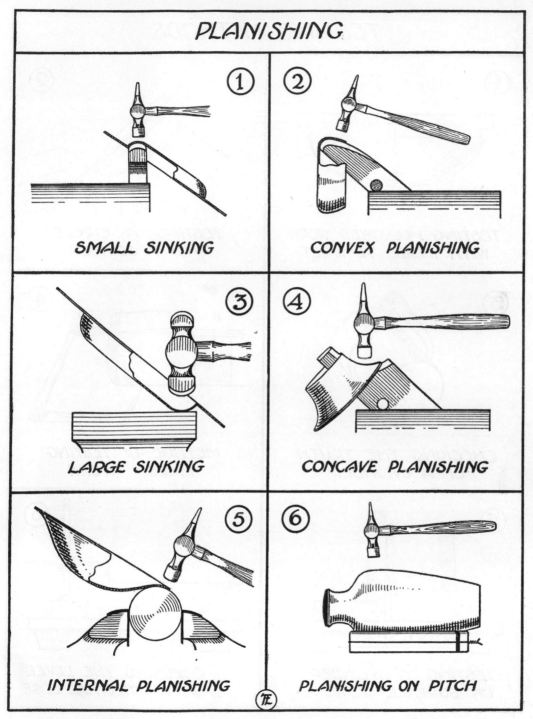

PLANISHING

1. SMALL SINKING

2. CONVEX PLANISHING

3. LARGE SINKING

4. CONCAVE PLANISHING

5. INTERNAL PLANISHING

6. PLANISHING ON PITCH

PLATE 29

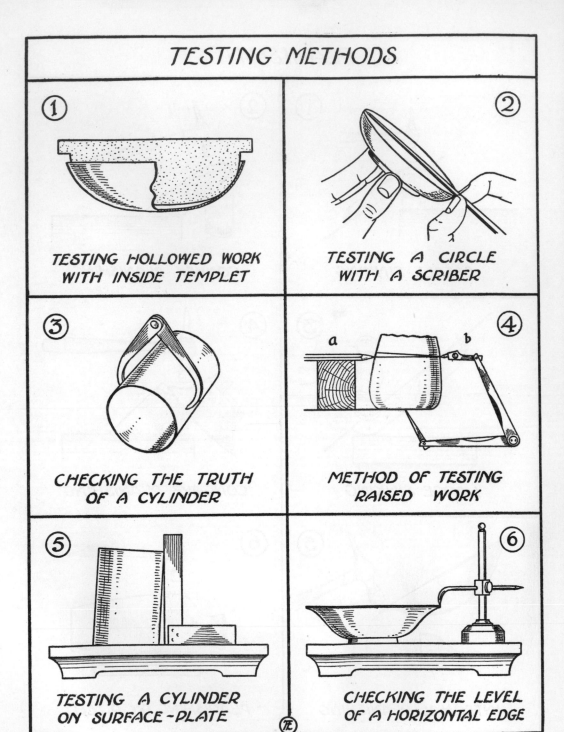

TESTING METHODS

1. TESTING HOLLOWED WORK WITH INSIDE TEMPLET

2. TESTING A CIRCLE WITH A SCRIBER

3. CHECKING THE TRUTH OF A CYLINDER

4. METHOD OF TESTING RAISED WORK

5. TESTING A CYLINDER ON SURFACE-PLATE

6. CHECKING THE LEVEL OF A HORIZONTAL EDGE

PLATE 30

226

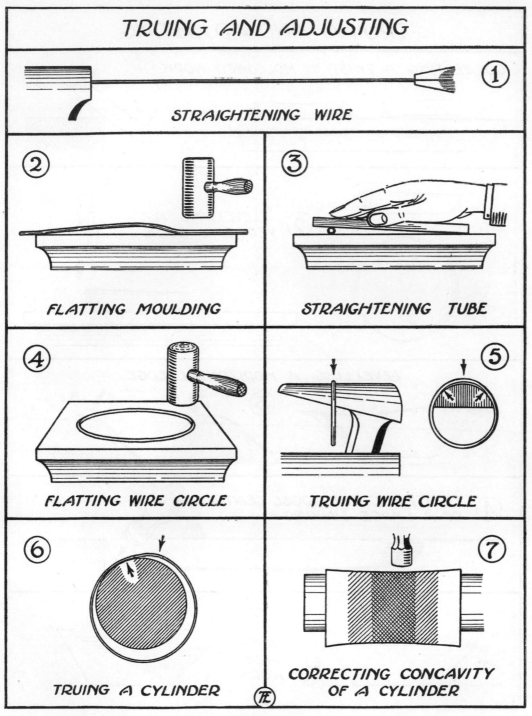

TRUING AND ADJUSTING

1. STRAIGHTENING WIRE

2. FLATTING MOULDING

3. STRAIGHTENING TUBE

4. FLATTING WIRE CIRCLE

5. TRUING WIRE CIRCLE

6. TRUING A CYLINDER

7. CORRECTING CONCAVITY OF A CYLINDER

PLATE 31

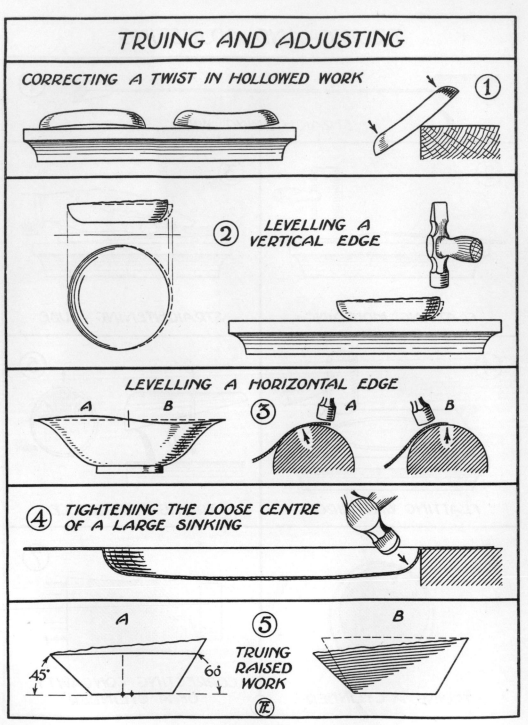

TRUING AND ADJUSTING

CORRECTING A TWIST IN HOLLOWED WORK ①

② **LEVELLING A VERTICAL EDGE**

LEVELLING A HORIZONTAL EDGE

A   B

③   A   B

④ **TIGHTENING THE LOOSE CENTRE OF A LARGE SINKING**

A   ⑤ **TRUING RAISED WORK**   B

45°   60°

PLATE 32

228

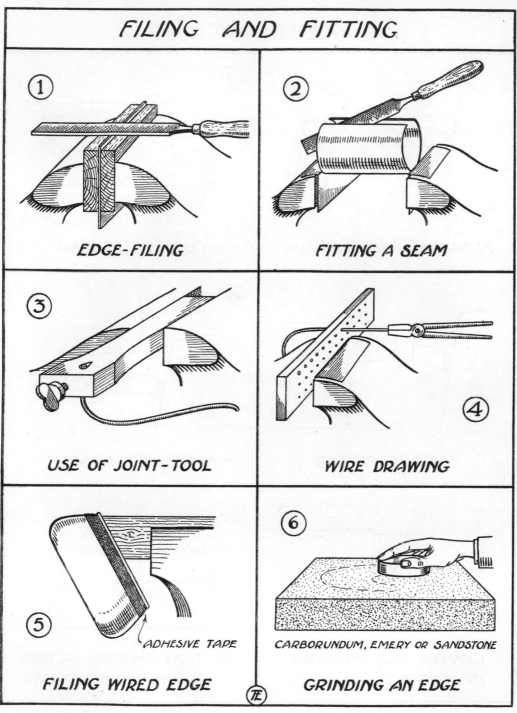

FILING AND FITTING

① EDGE-FILING

② FITTING A SEAM

③ USE OF JOINT-TOOL

④ WIRE DRAWING

⑤ FILING WIRED EDGE — ADHESIVE TAPE

⑥ GRINDING AN EDGE — CARBORUNDUM, EMERY OR SANDSTONE

PLATE 33

229

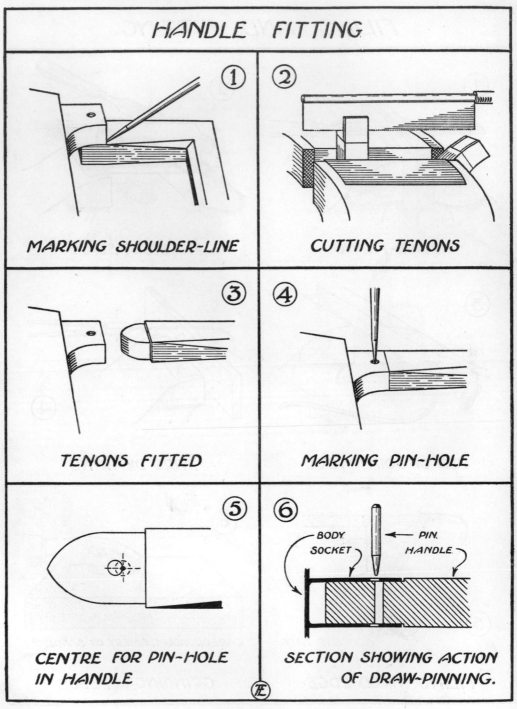

HANDLE FITTING

① MARKING SHOULDER-LINE

② CUTTING TENONS

③ TENONS FITTED

④ MARKING PIN-HOLE

⑤ CENTRE FOR PIN-HOLE IN HANDLE

⑥ SECTION SHOWING ACTION OF DRAW-PINNING.

BODY.
SOCKET.
PIN.
HANDLE.

PLATE 34

230

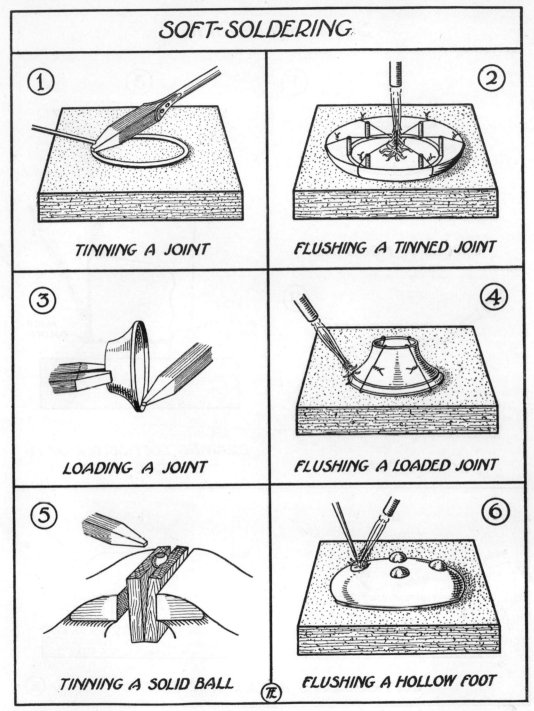

SOFT-SOLDERING

① TINNING A JOINT

② FLUSHING A TINNED JOINT

③ LOADING A JOINT

④ FLUSHING A LOADED JOINT

⑤ TINNING A SOLID BALL

⑥ FLUSHING A HOLLOW FOOT

PLATE 35

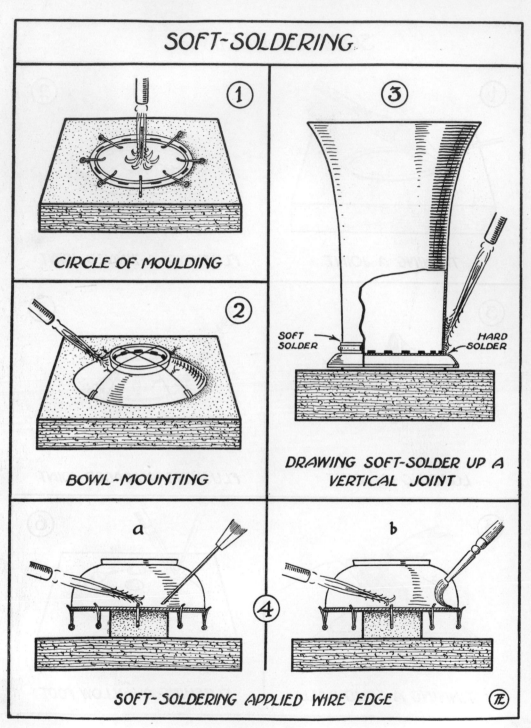

SOFT-SOLDERING

1 CIRCLE OF MOULDING

2 BOWL-MOUNTING

3 DRAWING SOFT-SOLDER UP A VERTICAL JOINT

SOFT SOLDER

HARD SOLDER

4 **a** **b** SOFT-SOLDERING APPLIED WIRE EDGE

PLATE 36

232

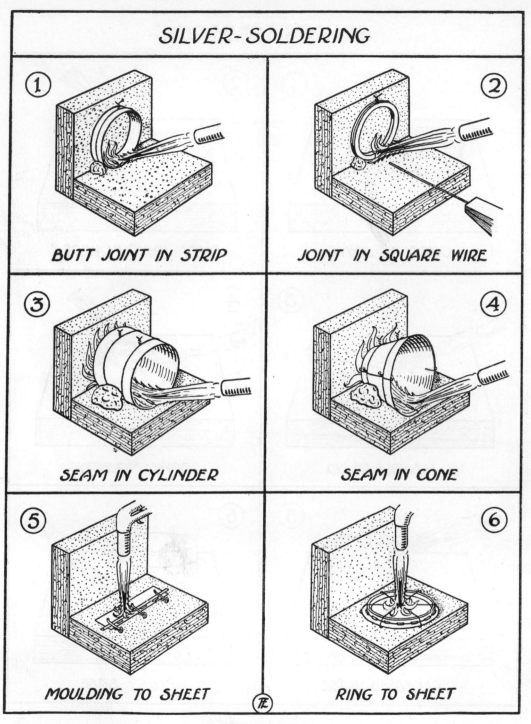

SILVER-SOLDERING

1. BUTT JOINT IN STRIP

2. JOINT IN SQUARE WIRE

3. SEAM IN CYLINDER

4. SEAM IN CONE

5. MOULDING TO SHEET

6. RING TO SHEET

PLATE 37

233

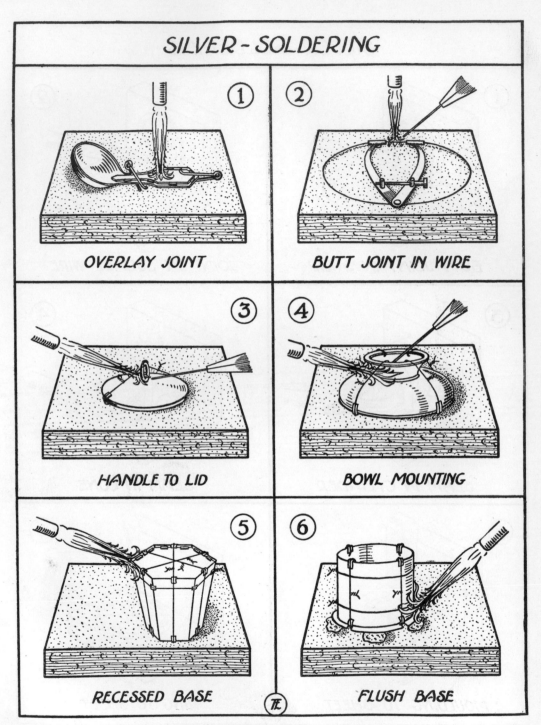

SILVER - SOLDERING

① OVERLAY JOINT

② BUTT JOINT IN WIRE

③ HANDLE TO LID

④ BOWL MOUNTING

⑤ RECESSED BASE

⑥ FLUSH BASE

PLATE 38

234

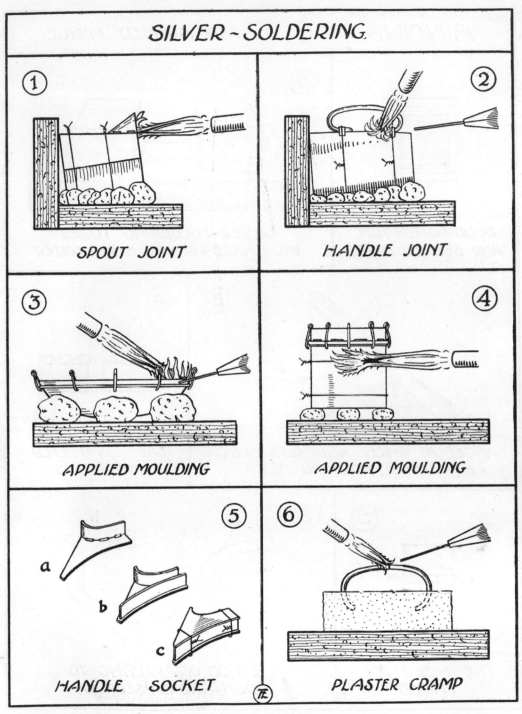

SILVER - SOLDERING.

1. SPOUT JOINT

2. HANDLE JOINT

3. APPLIED MOULDING

4. APPLIED MOULDING

5. HANDLE SOCKET

6. PLASTER CRAMP

PLATE 39

235

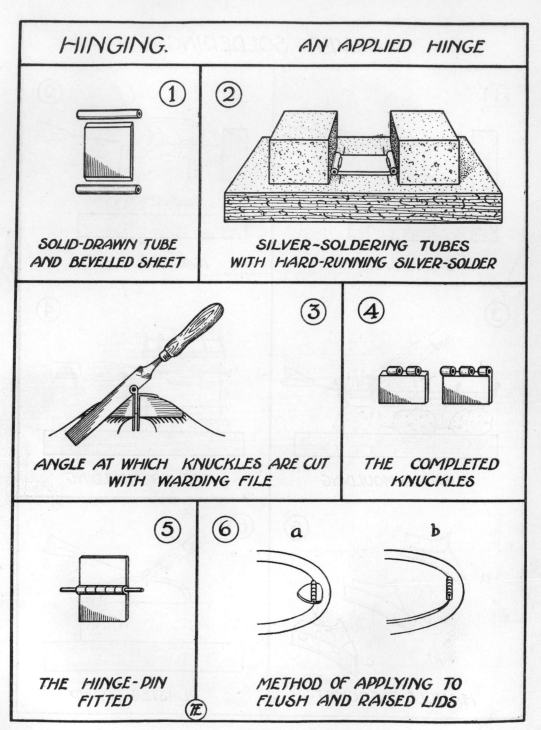

HINGING. **AN APPLIED HINGE**

① SOLID-DRAWN TUBE AND BEVELLED SHEET

② SILVER-SOLDERING TUBES WITH HARD-RUNNING SILVER-SOLDER

③ ANGLE AT WHICH KNUCKLES ARE CUT WITH WARDING FILE

④ THE COMPLETED KNUCKLES

⑤ THE HINGE-PIN FITTED

⑥ a b METHOD OF APPLYING TO FLUSH AND RAISED LIDS

PLATE 40

236

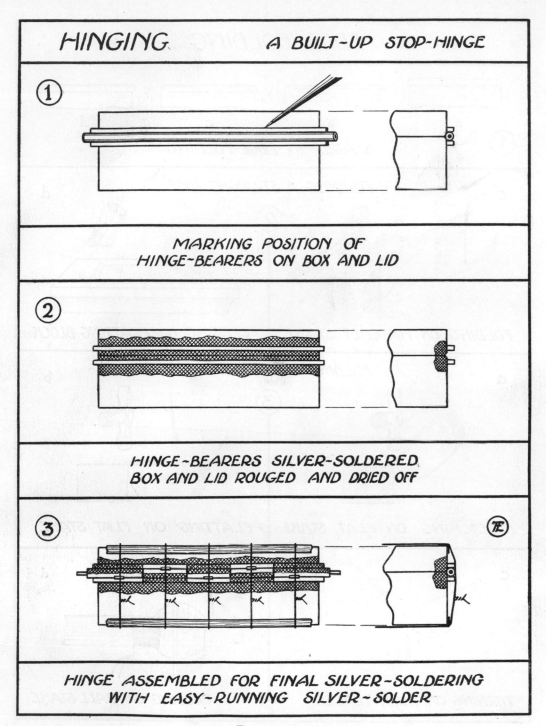

HINGING. A BUILT-UP STOP-HINGE

1 MARKING POSITION OF
HINGE-BEARERS ON BOX AND LID

2 HINGE-BEARERS SILVER-SOLDERED.
BOX AND LID ROUGED AND DRIED OFF

3 HINGE ASSEMBLED FOR FINAL SILVER-SOLDERING
WITH EASY-RUNNING SILVER-SOLDER

PLATE 41

237

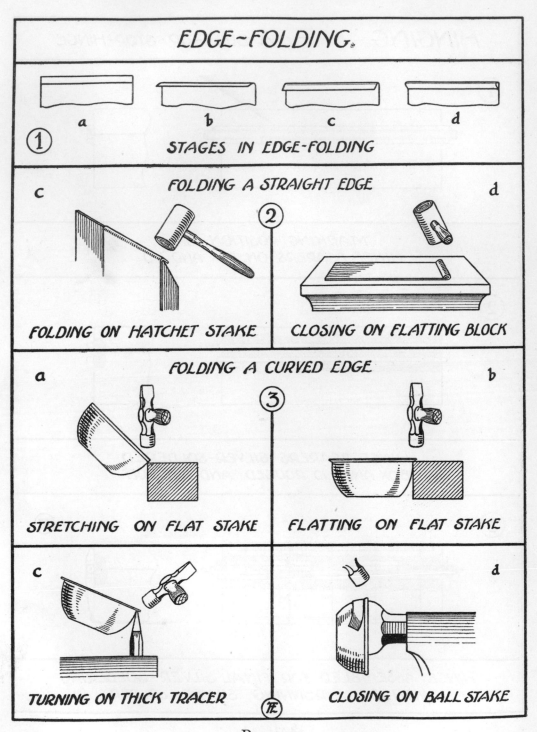

EDGE-FOLDING.

① STAGES IN EDGE-FOLDING

a   b   c   d

② FOLDING A STRAIGHT EDGE

c

FOLDING ON HATCHET STAKE

d

CLOSING ON FLATTING BLOCK

③ FOLDING A CURVED EDGE

a

STRETCHING ON FLAT STAKE

b

FLATTING ON FLAT STAKE

c

TURNING ON THICK TRACER

d

CLOSING ON BALL STAKE

PLATE 42

238

EDGE-WIRING

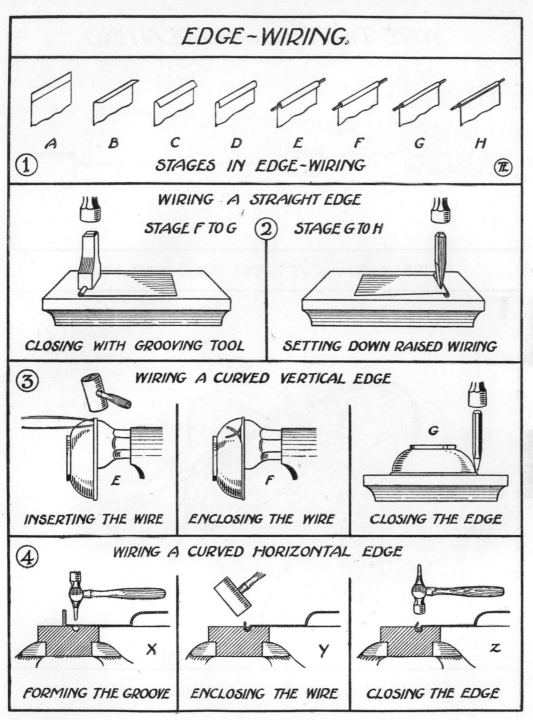

A B C D E F G H

① STAGES IN EDGE-WIRING

WIRING A STRAIGHT EDGE

STAGE F TO G ② STAGE G TO H

CLOSING WITH GROOVING TOOL

SETTING DOWN RAISED WIRING

③ WIRING A CURVED VERTICAL EDGE

E

INSERTING THE WIRE

F

ENCLOSING THE WIRE

G

CLOSING THE EDGE

④ WIRING A CURVED HORIZONTAL EDGE

X

FORMING THE GROOVE

Y

ENCLOSING THE WIRE

Z

CLOSING THE EDGE

PLATE 43

WIRE TWISTING AND PLAITING

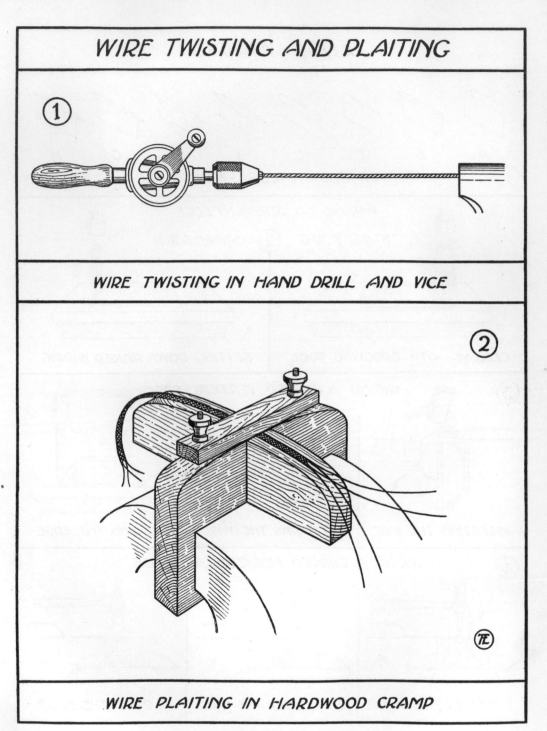

① WIRE TWISTING IN HAND DRILL AND VICE

② WIRE PLAITING IN HARDWOOD CRAMP

PLATE 44

SURFACE DECORATION

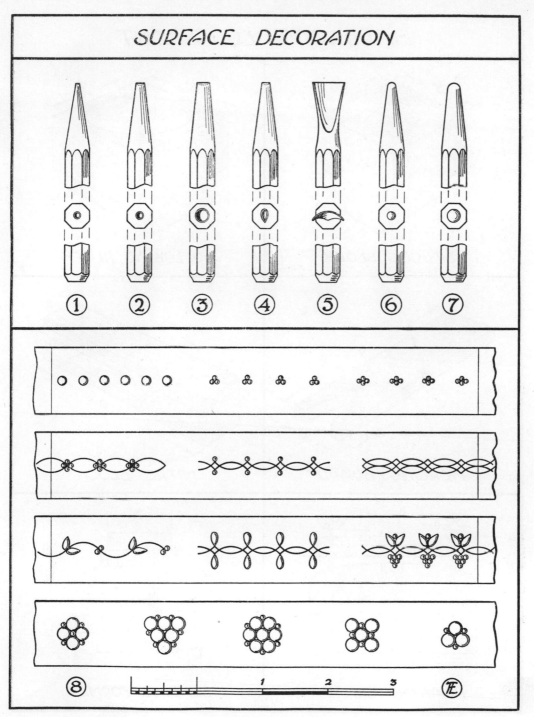

PLATE 45

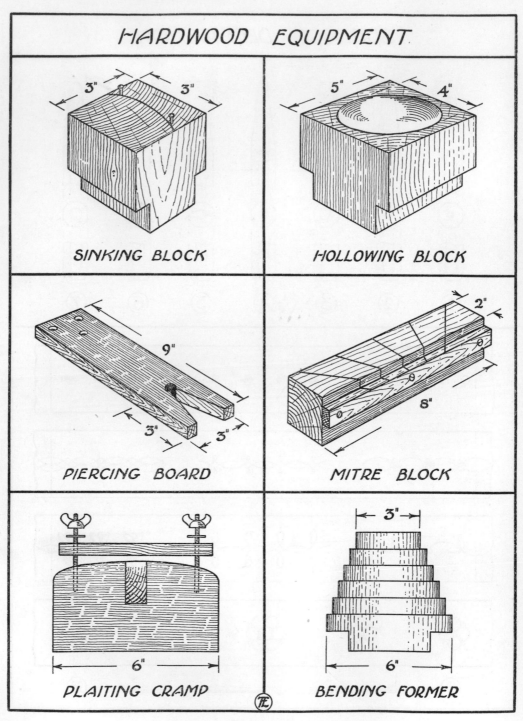

HARDWOOD EQUIPMENT

SINKING BLOCK

HOLLOWING BLOCK

PIERCING BOARD

MITRE BLOCK

PLAITING CRAMP

BENDING FORMER

PLATE 46

242

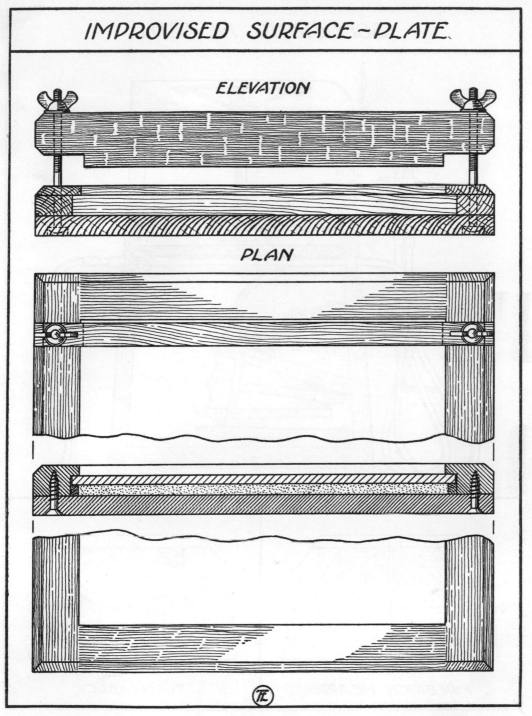

IMPROVISED SURFACE~PLATE.

ELEVATION

PLAN

PLATE 47

SOLDERING HEARTH

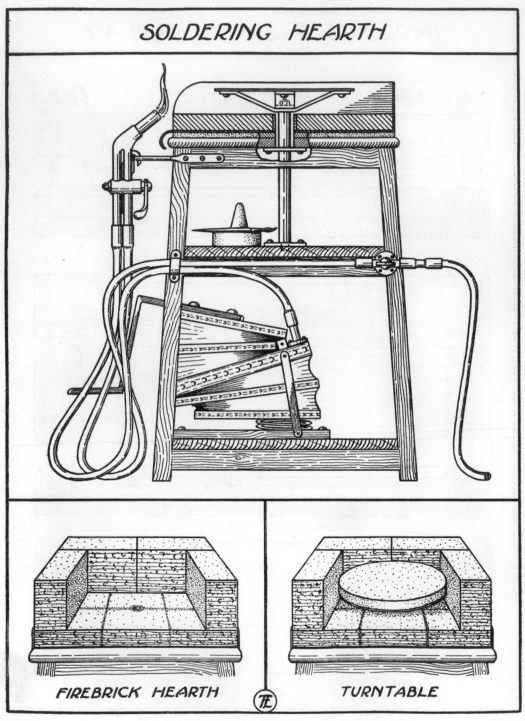

FIREBRICK HEARTH   TURNTABLE

PLATE 48

244

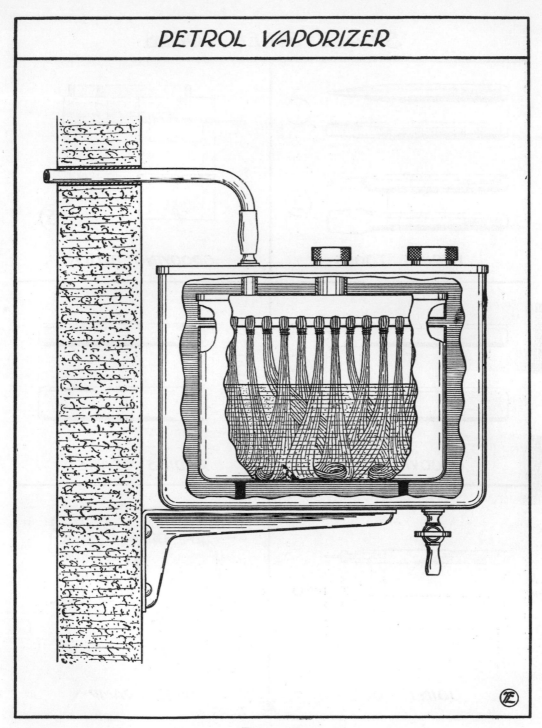

PLATE 49

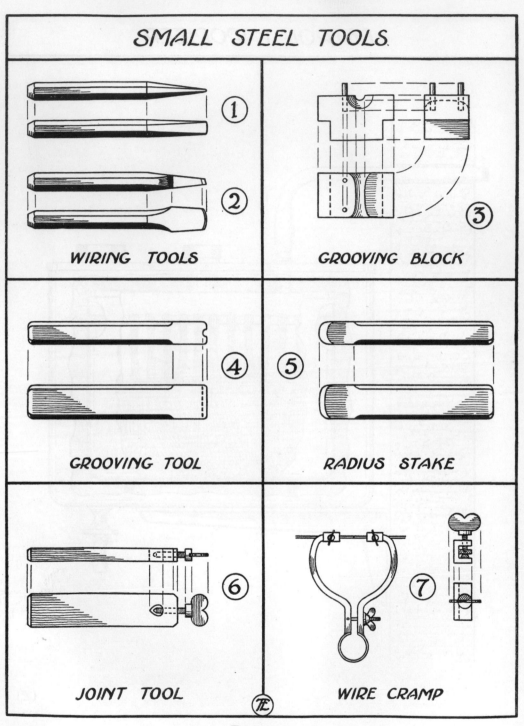

SMALL STEEL TOOLS.

① ②
WIRING TOOLS

③
GROOVING BLOCK

④ ⑤
GROOVING TOOL   RADIUS STAKE

⑥ ⑦
JOINT TOOL   WIRE CRAMP

PLATE 50

246

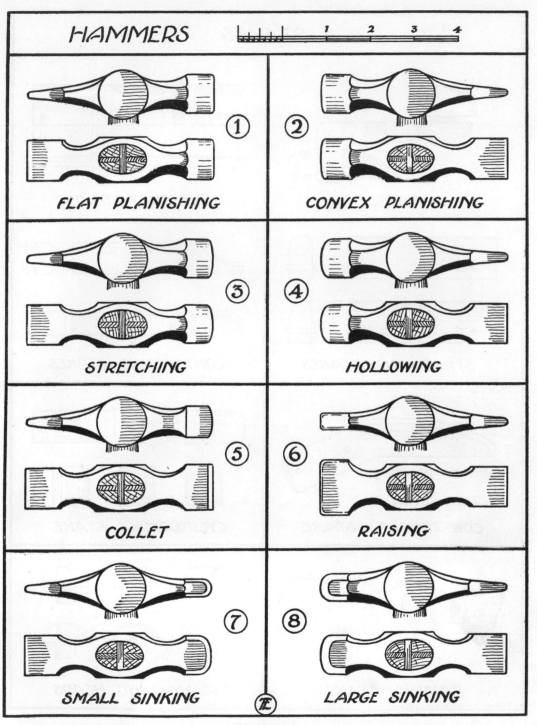

HAMMERS

FLAT PLANISHING ① ② CONVEX PLANISHING

STRETCHING ③ ④ HOLLOWING

COLLET ⑤ ⑥ RAISING

SMALL SINKING ⑦ ⑧ LARGE SINKING

PLATE 51

247

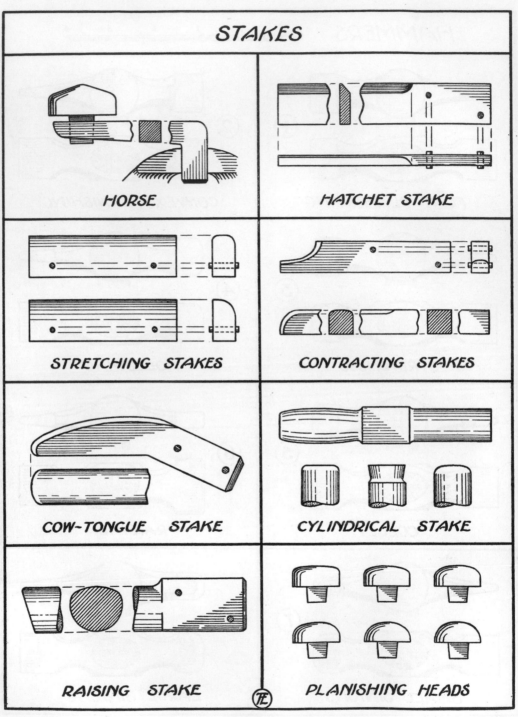

STAKES

HORSE

HATCHET STAKE

STRETCHING STAKES

CONTRACTING STAKES

COW-TONGUE STAKE

CYLINDRICAL STAKE

RAISING STAKE

PLANISHING HEADS

PLATE 52

248

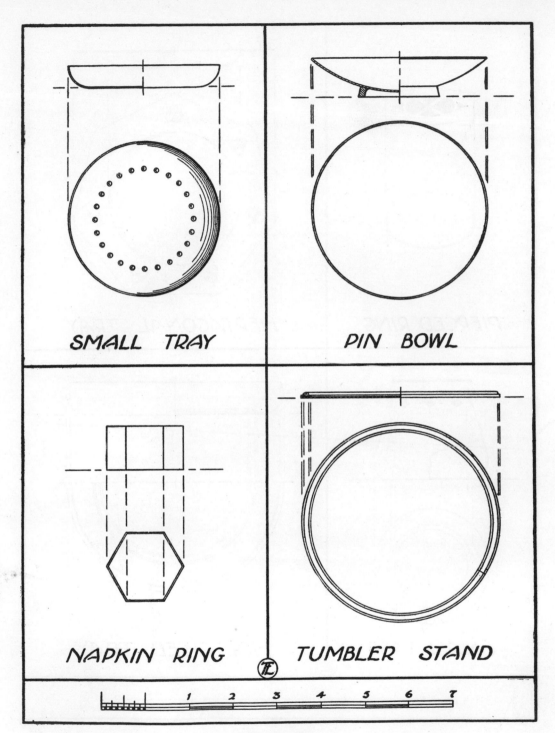

SMALL TRAY

PIN BOWL

NAPKIN RING

TUMBLER STAND

PLATE 53

249

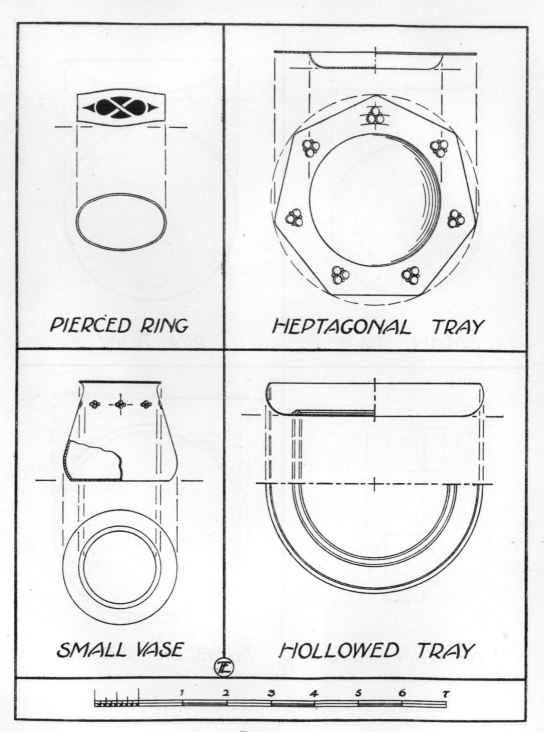

PIERCED RING

HEPTAGONAL TRAY

SMALL VASE

HOLLOWED TRAY

1   2   3   4   5   6   7

PLATE 54

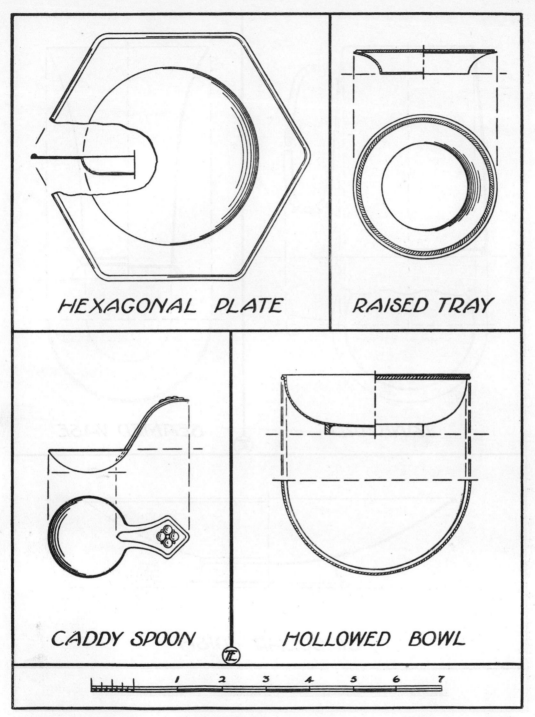

HEXAGONAL PLATE

RAISED TRAY

CADDY SPOON

HOLLOWED BOWL

1 2 3 4 5 6 7

PLATE 55

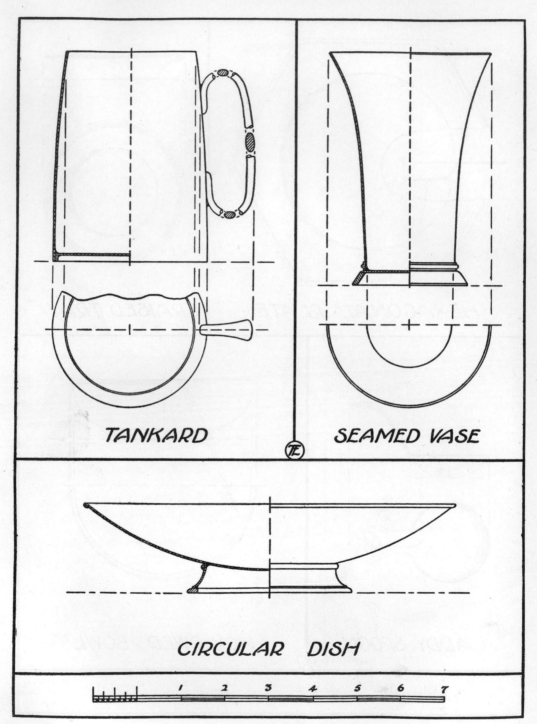

TANKARD

SEAMED VASE

CIRCULAR DISH

1 *2* *3* *4* *5* *6* *7*

PLATE 56

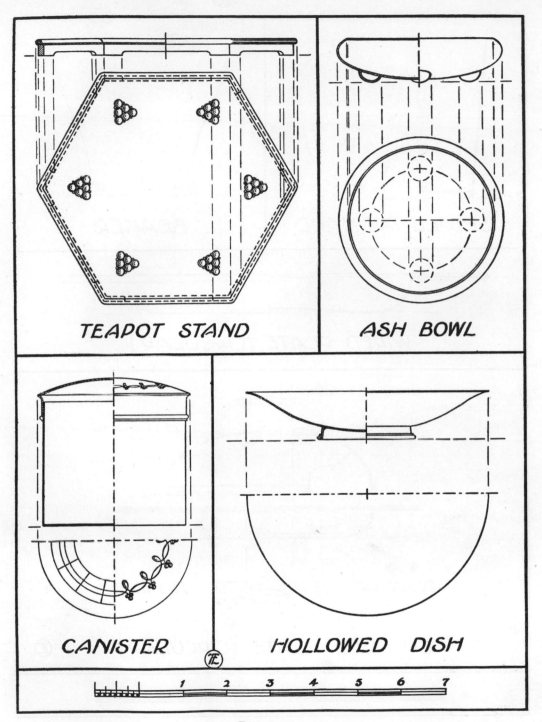

TEAPOT STAND

ASH BOWL

CANISTER

HOLLOWED DISH

1 2 3 4 5 6 7

PLATE 57

253

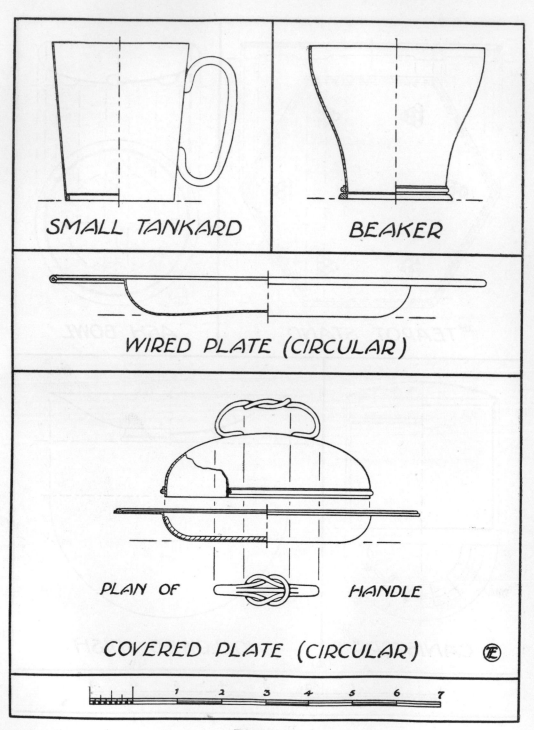

SMALL TANKARD

BEAKER

WIRED PLATE (CIRCULAR)

PLAN OF   HANDLE

COVERED PLATE (CIRCULAR)

PLATE 58

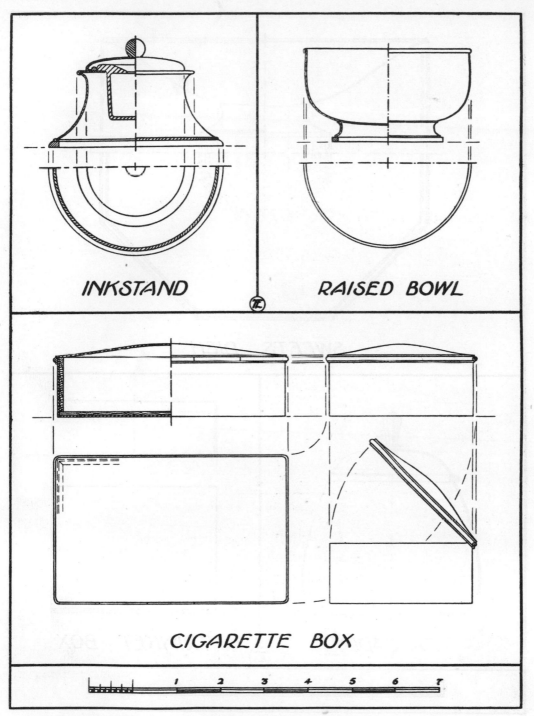

INKSTAND

RAISED BOWL

CIGARETTE BOX

PLATE 59

255

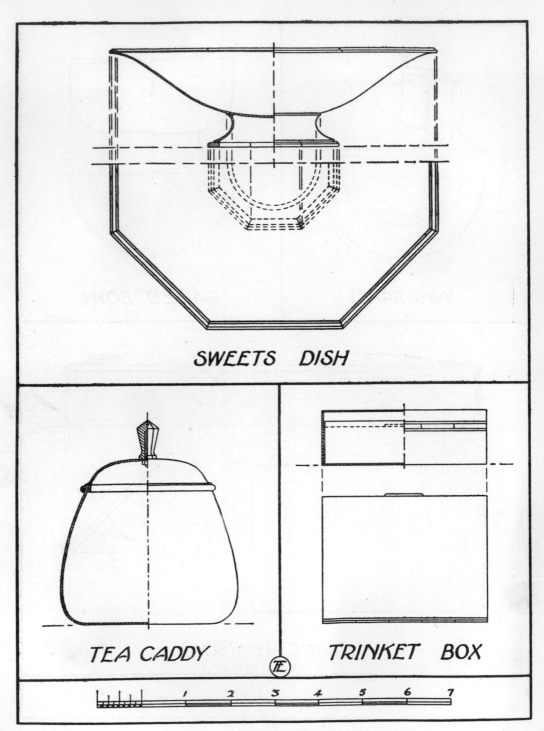

SWEETS DISH

TEA CADDY

TRINKET BOX

1 2 3 4 5 6 7

PLATE 60

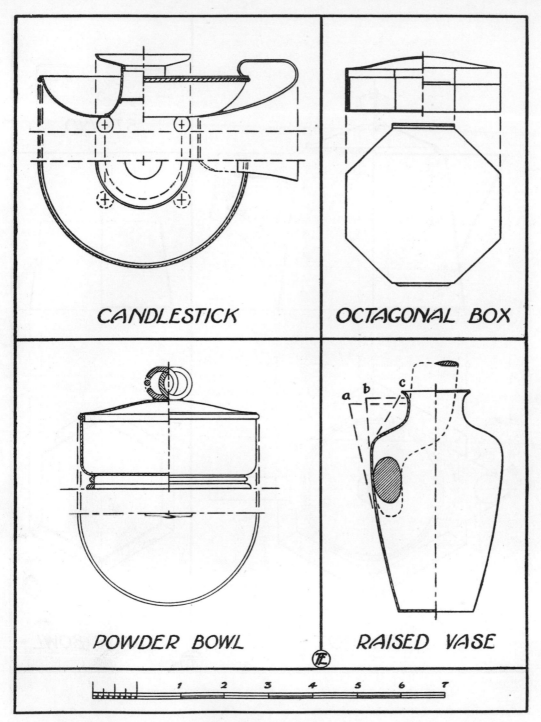

CANDLESTICK

OCTAGONAL BOX

POWDER BOWL

RAISED VASE

PLATE 61

257

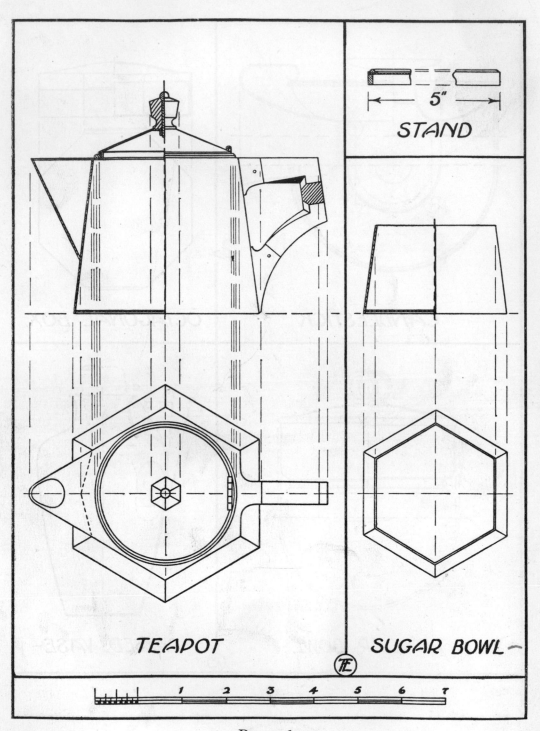

STAND

TEAPOT

SUGAR BOWL

1 2 3 4 5 6 7

PLATE 62

258

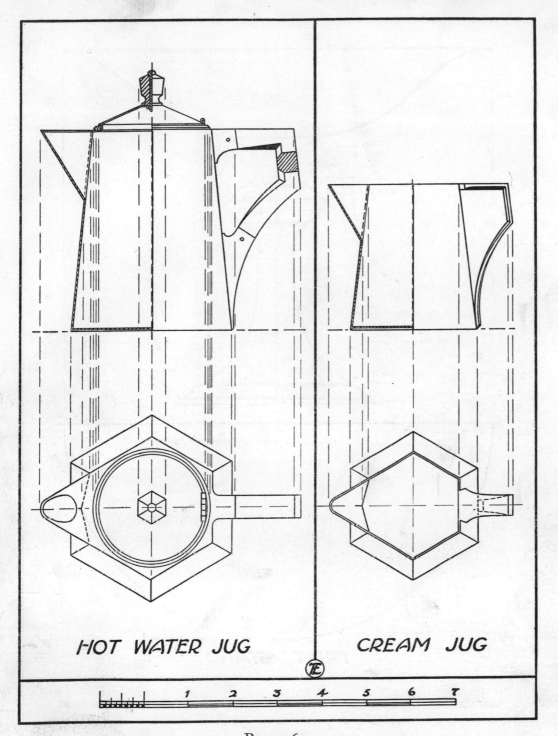

HOT WATER JUG   CREAM JUG

1   2   3   4   5   6   7

Plate 63

259

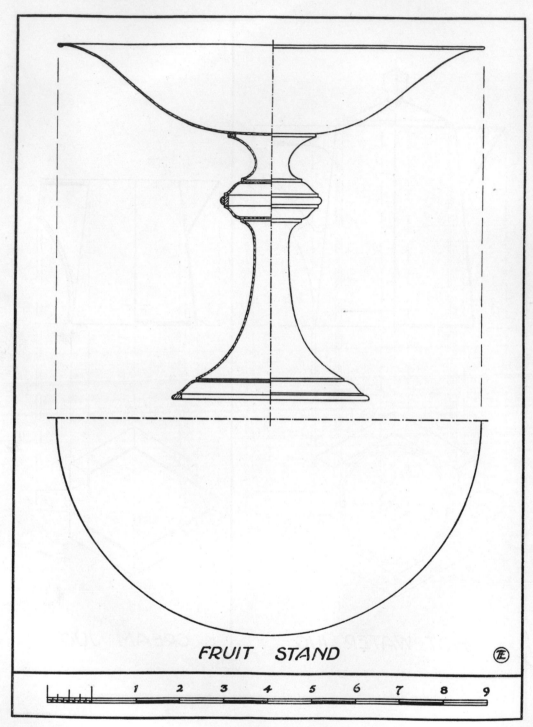

FRUIT STAND

| | 1 | 2 | 3 | 4 | 5 | 6 | 7 | 8 | 9 |

PLATE 64

260

PLATE 65

TUMBLER STAND

NAPKIN RING   SMALL TRAY

PIN BOWL

PLATE 66

HEPTAGONAL TRAY

SMALL VASE PIERCED RING

HOLLOWED TRAY

PLATE 67

HEXAGONAL PLATE
HOLLOWED BOWL
RAISED TRAY   CADDY SPOON

PLATE 68

SEAMED VASE   TANKARD

CIRCULAR DISH

PLATE 69

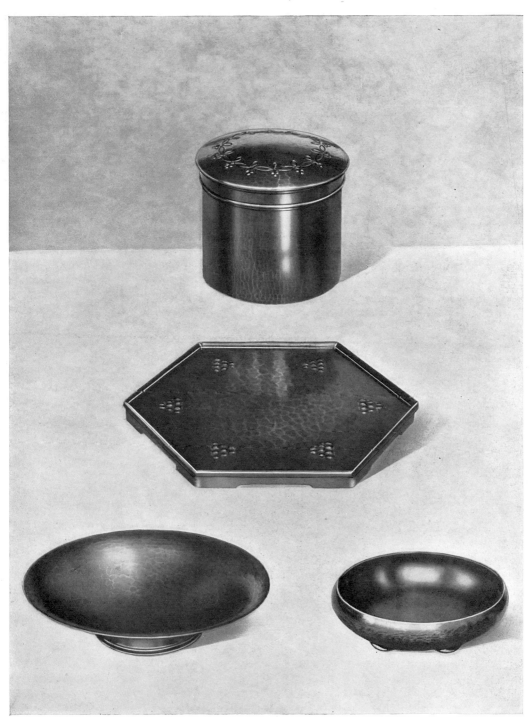

CANISTER

TEAPOT STAND

HOLLOWED DISH   ASH BOWL

PLATE 70

WIRED PLATE

BEAKER   SMALL TANKARD

COVERED PLATE

PLATE 71

INK STAND   CIGARETTE BOX

RAISED BOWL

PLATE 72

TEA CADDY   SWEETS DISH

TRINKET BOX

PLATE 73

RAISED VASE

POWDER BOWL   OCTAGONAL BOX

CANDLESTICK

PLATE 74

HOT-WATER JUG   SUGAR BOWL

TEAPOT   CREAM JUG

STAND

PLATE 75

FRUIT STAND

PLATE 76

RAISED SILVER VASE